THE WORLD YOU INHERIT

Books by John Gabriel Navarra

CLOCKS, CALENDARS, AND CARROUSELS

FROM GENERATION TO GENERATION

OUR NOISY WORLD

A TURTLE IN THE HOUSE

WIDE WORLD WEATHER

THE WORLD YOU INHERIT

JOHN GABRIEL NAVARRA

The World You Inherit:
A STORY
OF POLLUTION

Published for
The American Museum of Natural History
The Natural History Press
Garden City, New York

The Natural History Press, publisher for The American Museum of Natural History, is a division of Doubleday & Company, Inc. Directed by a joint editorial board made up of members of the staff of both the Museum and Doubleday, the Natural History Press publishes books and periodicals in all branches of the life and earth sciences, including anthropology and astronomy. The Natural History Press has its editorial offices at The American Museum of Natural History, Central Park West at 79th Street, New York, N.Y. 10024, and its business offices at 501 Franklin Avenue, Garden City, N.Y. 11530.

First Edition

New York City is below. Even when viewed from an altitude of eighteen-thousand feet, there is evidence of pollution.

PREFACE

Will our natural environment be able to support life in the twenty-first century? There is every indication that catastrophe is lurking around the corner. The rapid increase in pollution of sky, land, and water is propelling us toward a climax of dangerous environmental conditions. No one can accurately portray the consequences, but this we do know: Man is the culprit, and only he can prevent the devastation and destruction. But to do this, there must be an awakening to the problem and decisive action on the part of all men. At times, this seems to be an impossible task!

During the last seventy years, the conservationists in the United States have wrought miracles: Important tracts of land have been set aside as national parks and forests; lumber companies have been persuaded to replant and harvest rather than to ravish and deplete; species of birds have been brought back from the edge of extinction; and even the bison and the antelope have been saved. These are truly great achievements. The men and women who accomplished them deserve our gratitude.

But there are monumental tasks that remain undone. The winds that whip around our earth lift and carry precious topsoil, dropping it hither and yon. Water overruns the banks of rivers and, when it recedes, leaves the scars of erosion and devastation. The air that sweeps across our land is getting filthier with each passing day. And, with all the righteous indignation of the last few years, too many people are not really accepting the task of cleansing the air of smoke, soot, and smog. Nor has there been any great progress made with the unpleasant tasks of freeing our waters from pollution and disposing of our solid wastes. Each of these conditions is a threat to the existence of man and brings his ability to survive into question. We should fear these insidious threats to our survival as much as we fear the more obvious holocaust of war.

JOHN GABRIEL NAVARRA

CONTENTS

THE WORLD YOU INHERIT

Chapter 1

MAN AND THE NATURAL ENVIRONMENT

At one time in the distant past, man and the natural environment were in harmony. Man was not set apart from the other animals that roamed the earth. He picked berries and hunted. Like the other creatures of the woods, hills, and plains, man kept himself alive by taking only what was needed for food and shelter. He lived and died, and his presence caused very little disturbance in the environment.

Gradually, however, man set himself apart from the other animals. He invented agriculture and became dependent on seeds, soil, rain, and the seasons. He began to harness animal power, too. Man became "master" and "keeper." He kept horses, cows, and oxen. Elephants, camels, sheep, goats, and other animals became part of the menagerie that man used. Thus man, the "interferer," was born. He denied freedom to animals he found useful, gradually changed their characteristics through breeding, and made them dependent on him.

Where man settled down to work the soil and farm, villages, towns, and cities eventually grew. The nonfarmers—the butcher, the baker, and the candlestickmaker—populated these villages. And all these people needed food. So the farmer opened new lands to harvest more crops to feed and to clothe the growing population of the urban centers. Many of the early farming practices depleted and ravaged the land. Thus man, the "spoiler," was born.

But it was the invention of machines that pushed man into a wild, uncontrolled era of exploitation and devastation of the environment. With the beginning of the Industrial Revolution, man hacked at and changed the landscape in significant ways. His factories dotted the countryside and crowded one upon the other in the cities. To feed his factories, man roamed and searched the earth for raw materials. He invented ways of gouging minerals and other prizes from the land and transporting them cheaply and economically to the industrial centers to build the new products of civilization.

With each improvement in material well-being, the population grew and the increasing multitudes spread across the face of the earth. Today, the population of the world increases at the rate of about 180,000 people each day. At the end of each month there are approximately five and a half million new people on the earth. This is really a staggering increase.

Think of the problem posed by the monthly addition to the world population: Let's imagine we could isolate the new people each month. In order to do so, we would need to create some rather large cities. In fact, we would need to build twelve new cities each year to house the monthly increase of five and a half million. And each city would need to be approximately as large as Chicago. Imagine the additional space, food, water, and health services needed to accommodate the populations of these twelve new cities. It all adds up to a mighty big problem.

The fact is that we do have this increase each month. And whether or not we construct new cities, we need to provide new housing, more food, more water, as well as health services and waste disposal facilities for these additional people. It is a tremendous task we have just to keep up with the needs of an expanding population. We need to plan, build, and move faster than we have if we are to meet these new needs as well as improve the condition of those people already a part of the world population.

Man long ago lost his status as a hunter living within the natural environment without disturbing it. The clearing of land, for example, to plant crops changed woodlands into grasslands. The eastern United States at the time of Columbus was covered with forests of hardwood trees. As the early colonists arrived, the forests were gradually replaced by farms, towns, and cities. Today the hardwood forests have all but disappeared.

We cannot, by any stretch of the imagination, return to the status of hunter and to the primitive methods of survival, which leave the environment undisturbed. Today the demands of an expanding world population for food and housing cannot be satisfied without affecting and changing the natural environment. But what we can do is to make our demands on the environment in more intelligent ways and with more concern for the consequences. We can also guard against the "robber practices" of the past, as, for example, meeting the demand for lumber to satisfy housing needs by the wanton destruction of vast forests. The lumber barons of the nineteenth and early twentieth centuries cut trees indiscriminately, without giving any thought to replanting. Huge profits were made, but the loss to the nation cannot be replaced by mere dollars.

Time is running out! Centuries of gouging the land and improper disposal of wastes have devastated and polluted vast areas of our planet. The by-products of our industry and our mechanized society have produced significant changes in the natural environment. We cannot re-create the unspoiled lands of yesteryear, but there is an urgent need to improve the situation.

And, although it is a matter of survival for man, the attempts at improvement are sporadic and do little more than reduce the rate at which conditions worsen. The problem is not one of the cities or of a region. It is a national problem, but one that can only be really solved by international planning. World environmental conditions must be changed for the better rather than simply modified to decrease the rate by which we are approaching catastrophe. Somehow we must learn to "march in step" with nature!

It is often easier to know that something is wrong than to know what to do about it. The sensory evidence of air pollution, for example, makes it obvious that a problem exists. And this problem can be seen and smelled in every major urban area in the United States and, for that matter, throughout the world.

Los Angeles is the classic example of automotive smog that chokes and burns. Thirty years ago, Pittsburgh literally disappeared under a pall of smoke. Today Pittsburgh has re-emerged but not really cleansed itself, since the "old smoke" has been replaced by more complex problems of air pollution that seem to defy correction. The 630-foot stainless steel arch that towers over St. Louis is, on more than a few occasions, obliterated from view by air pollution from both Missouri and Illinois. The mountain

New Orleans is thousands of feet below us. The pollution lifting skyward from the stack of the factory dominates our view and makes a sewer of the sky.

air of Denver—once famed for its clear, pure quality—is subject to smog. And the clear desert air of Phoenix is gradually losing its clarity!

Of all the reckless activities of man, none is more shameful than the poisoning of our air. Freeways, factories, and more than seven million residents in Los Angeles County combine to produce smog thick enough to destroy vegetation on a grand scale. A two-day siege of heavy smog once ruined two hundred thousand dollars' worth of truck farm produce. At the end of the 1960s, there were still enough farmers to rank Los Angeles County twelfth in the United States in the value of its agricultural production. But the heavy smog buildup, which is common in the late fall, often makes plants look like a blowtorch has been passed over the leaves. The combination of traffic on the freeways, population, and pollution will most certainly cause agriculture to wither and die in that county. And the people will become dependent on farm produce shipped into the area.

Air is brought into our lungs in rather large amounts. We inhale and exhale approximately three thousand gallons of it each day. Pure air should contain only oxygen, nitrogen, water vapor, carbon dioxide, and the so-called rare gases. Today, however, the air that most of us breathe contains oxides of nitrogen and sulphur, as well as various kinds of dust and soot, particles of rubber and asbestos, huge amounts of carbon monoxide, and a vast array of organic compounds.

Approximately 150 million tons of pollutants were pumped into the air each year in the United States alone during the 1960s. Motor vehicles produced most of these pollutants; the second major source was industrial operations, with the generation of electric power as the third major contributor. Space heating (heating of homes, offices, etc.) and refuse disposal also made significant contributions of pollutants to the air.

By 1980, through the genius of assembly line production, we can expect an increase of 50 percent in the number of automobiles on the roads of the United States. Thus, the pollutants from this source will increase dramatically unless drastic control measures are enforced. But even with a complete redesign of the internal combustion engine and severe controls, it is estimated that there will be a steady climb in the amount of sulphur dioxide

emitted and that by 1980 the increase will be 75 percent above
current figures. This is especially frightening considering that sulphur dioxide is converted to corrosive sulphuric acid in the air.
There should be no doubt about the urgent need to attack the
problem of the pollution caused by the internal combustion engine.

The solution to this problem is really a matter of public choice.
People must first choose the kind of atmospheric environment
they wish to have. If the choice is to have a "clean" environment
and to retain the internal combustion engine, then money and
controls are needed to solve the problem. And if we are determined to have both—i.e., clean air and automobiles—we will find
that the cost is not prohibitive and that industry can supply the
needed solutions.

Electricity is an important source of energy for our society.
Fossil fuels and steam boilers are used to generate most of this
power today. The burning of fossil fuels—i.e., oil and coal—adds
significant amounts of pollutants to the air. In the future, the
need for electrical power will be even greater than it is today.
The pollutants pumped into the atmosphere by the generation of
electric power will double by 1980.

The solution for this dilemma is to convert our utility industry, i.e., instead of burning fossil fuels to use nuclear energy to
generate electricity. The switch to nuclear power would significantly decrease environmental pollution. But it takes time to convert huge installations. It cannot be done overnight. If we were
to start this conversion today, it would be difficult to have more
than 50 percent of our utility installations operating with nuclear
power by the year 2000. And this means that the very least we
can expect is another 100 percent increase in the amount of pollutants pumped into the air between 1980 and the year 2000.

Public demand and a new public policy could change this estimate. An aroused public and a determined national effort to get
the job done is the only real course to get these dismal expec-
tations to change dramatically. The public utility companies
need encouragement, incentive, and pressure to convert to nuclear power. It takes time to get things done. The time for action and decision is now—not ten years from now!

Air pollution is a killer. People become sick, and they die

from breathing dirty air. We may soon find that there is not enough air in the whole world to thin out the pollutants that pour upward from the world's industrial areas.

Air cannot be treated. You cannot take polluted air over a city and treat it so that it is made tolerable for man to breathe. The only possible way to control air pollution is at its source.

The prospects for the future seem to be dismal. Air is becoming more polluted. And there is every reason to believe that filth in the air will increase in the foreseeable future unless drastic action is taken. The diseases produced and the diseases aggravated by air pollution will rise even more rapidly as a result of a multiplying effect that causes the disease rate to increase faster than the pollution level itself. Thus, the need to mount an attack on pollutants in the air is of crucial importance to man and his survival.

Water—an important part of the natural environment—is crucial for man's survival. Water falls fresh from the sky as rain, snow, sleet, or hail. Some of it sinks into the earth and becomes ground water. Another portion runs across the land and forms streams and rivers. It is called surface water. Eventually, all the sky water that falls on the land works its way to the sea.

Fortunately for man, the water does not remain in the sea. The basins called oceans are but one stop in a cyclical journey that "pumps" water from the sea to the land and back to the sea again. The restless ocean gives its water back to the sky through the process of evaporation. The sky water is carried over the land as clouds, and some of it falls and again works its way across the land back to the sea. This series of events is called the hydrological cycle. It insures a constant, steady flow of fresh water pouring onto the land.

The total water supply for any country can be estimated by measuring the water that flows from its streams into the oceans each day. The assumption is that the water "going out" must have "come in." The water discharged into the oceans from the continental United States is about four and a half billion cubic meters, or one thousand billion gallons a day. Thus the total daily water supply for the United States is set at this figure.

During the decade of the 1960s, the total volume of water withdrawn by man per day averaged three hundred billion gal-

Sky water falls from clouds, runs across the earth, and works its way to the restless ocean.

lons. Of this amount, approximately two hundred billion gallons were returned to the streams, rivers, and lakes as polluted water after being used in industrial or household processes. Only six billion gallons per day were consumed or used in ways that withheld it from being returned immediately to the flow moving toward the oceans. Thus during this period in the United States the water withdrawn amounted to 30 percent of the supply available. And consuming-use was slightly more than 5 percent of the total supply.

Now you might look at these figures and say: "What's the problem? There is no water shortage. There is no crisis!" *And this might be true for today.* But let's look at the history of the situation: For centuries we have been misusing our waters. The polluted condition of streams, rivers, and lakes is ample evidence of this. In fact, we use 95 percent of the water available to us as a conveyor belt. We dump wastes into our rivers and hope that it will be carried out to sea. But downstream many communities must dip into these polluted conveyor systems to extract water for drinking, agricultural, industrial, and household uses. Water contamination is costly. Expensive technology must be applied to water treatment in order to secure fresh water. This means that the water bill gets bigger and bigger.

At the present time, we need not be concerned with the *quantity* of water available nationwide but rather with its *quality*. In the future, however, there may be a need to be concerned about quantity, too. By the year 2000, we will need to withdraw nine hundred billion gallons per day from the available supply. This figure is about 90 percent of the supply currently available. Of course, you must realize that water is used more than once on its way to the ocean. But, nevertheless, it is estimated that more than seven hundred billion gallons will be returned to the streams, rivers, and lakes as polluted water. This means that we may have enough water available, but we will need to limit the current practice of permitting each user to add pollution. The control of pollutants is the key to fresh water and the protection of its quality.

Look out over our land. Find the hills covered with towering trees; search out the meadows and grasslands. The view is pleasing to the eye and aesthetically satisfying. When the land is in bloom, we accept it, think nothing of the wonder of it, nor what needs to be done to preserve it. Today, however, we are confronted by land that is barren and heaped with junk. The ugliness makes us pause and wonder.

The trees, meadows, and grasslands depend on the soil—a complex system of living and nonliving materials. Soil is one of the most important material resources of any country. Its formation starts when the action of weather causes rocks to crack, splinter, and break. Gradually, the rock pieces become smaller and decay. Air contributes to soil formation too. The chemicals (oxygen, carbon dioxide, and water) that are found in air combine with the elements in rocks to change the characteristics of the rock particles. Then plants begin to grow in this crude soil. The roots of the plants extract minerals from the rocks and help to change the soil too. Old plants die, decay, and form humus. Then new plants follow and life goes on. Micro-organisms, such as bacteria, are also at work helping the process of decay. Animals, large and small, move and root through the soil, mixing it and enriching it by contributing wastes as well as their own bodies when they die.

Let's examine a plant growing in a wooded area. The plant converts nitrogen and other minerals found in the soil to sugars, fats, and proteins. Nitrates are particularly crucial to plant growth. In the natural environment, nitrogen reaches the soil as a result of the work of bacteria. The natural concentration of nitrogen in the soil is very low, and it is held in a stable, organic form. Thus the roots of plants must search it out and work to pull the nitrogen into the leaves, where it is converted and changed to protein material. In order for the roots to do their job properly, they must be well supplied with oxygen. But oxygen reaches the roots only if the soil is porous. And the porous soil structure depends on the presence of humus. So you see that there is a fine balance needed to maintain porosity, oxygen, and organic nitrogen content of the soil.

When Columbus opened the Americas for exploration, the soil system was in natural balance. Huge forests and grasslands flourished. The men who came began to farm in the rich soil. They placed plants closer and in greater numbers than ordinarily found in nature. These early farmers had no artificial program of adding nutrients to the soil, and so the store of soil minerals gradually depleted. As the crop yields declined year by year, the farmers simply moved westward, cleared new land, and planted new crops. This was, of course, a wasteful process. The organic content of the soil declined year after year, and its productivity declined, too.

The folly of this process was eventually recognized and, gradually, animal manures and imported fertilizers, such as guano, were used to return nutrients to the soil. As a response to a recognized need, the growing chemical industry developed manmade fertilizers. By 1940, there was a great movement toward the use of these cheaper, inorganic fertilizers. Thus huge amounts of nitrogen, phosphorus, potassium, and other plant nutrients began to be added to the soil.

The use of fertilizers increases the crop yield. Today, fewer farmers working fewer acres are able to produce a more abundant food supply than was possible a century ago. And this additional food is needed to satisfy the hunger of a growing world population. It can be put to good use.

The wide application of manmade fertilizers, however, is a mixed blessing. Their use provides a bounty of food; but it also destroys the natural soil balance of nutrients, oxygen, and humus. This leads to some serious problems. During heavy rains, for example, the inorganic fertilizer, especially the nitrogen portion, washes out of the soil into streams, rivers, and lakes. Estimates indicate that as much as 25 percent of the applied fertilizer is washed out of the soil. Another 10 percent leaves the soil as volatile nitrogen oxides and ammonia. These volatile nitrogen compounds are produced as a result of bacterial action that is stimulated by the excess nitrogen and insufficient amounts of oxygen in the soil. Eventually, these volatile nitrogen compounds fall to earth along with the rain.

The excess nitrogen washed out of the soil is a severe threat to the environment. It contributes to the problem of water pollution because huge amounts of nitrogen in water cause overgrowths of algae. And the algae growing and dying at rapid rates produce their own cycle of organic pollution. One small event can cause a whole series of difficulties when you are dealing with the delicate balance of nature. The magnitude of the excess nitrogen problem can be sensed when you realize that in the late 1960s agriculture added as much nitrogen to surface waters as did municipal sewage.

Then don't forget that on top of all these problems of land and soil management, we literally add the burden of garbage. We discard bottles, cans, wastepaper, junked automobiles, plastic containers, and an almost unending array of dazzling trinkets and smelly trash. In the United States alone, more than five and a half billion pounds of refuse await disposal each week.

By no means should we consider garbage the special problem of the city dweller. The urban center is not alone. There are large surpluses of plant and animal wastes in most agricultural communities. And don't forget the leaves, scraps, the trash from suburbia, as well as the solid wastes from industrial plants that dot the countryside. Disposal, generally, is not handled as well in the country as it is in the city. This is quite obvious to us when we smell the aroma of burning leaves from an open fire or of baking garbage in a homemade incinerator.

We discard automobiles in the most unlikely places.

Currently, solid wastes are disposed of by landfill or by in-cineration. But even with incineration, something must be done with the residue. Burying garbage itself or the residue after incineration means that vacant land must be available. And in most communities we are running out of this kind of space. Then there is a further difficulty; the burial of garbage or its residue can lead to the pollution of important supplies of ground water.

The problem is complex. The complicated biology of the soil, the need for food, and the accumulation of wastes from home, farm, and industry bind us together. With respect to pollution, the countryside, the woodlands, the city, the industrial plant, and the farm must have the same fate. We cannot think ex-clusively of any one of these if we are genuinely concerned about the condition of the environment.

The world ocean surrounds and engulfs each of the continents. The streams and rivers flowing across the land have served as conveyor belts used by man and nature to transport wastes to the sea. This accessibility of the ocean has made it a convenient receptacle for waste disposal.

At one time man thought he could cast off smoke casually into the sky and sewage into the rivers. This worked for a long time because there were vast reserves of pure air and fresh water that easily diluted the pollutants. But as man and his wastes have increased, difficulties have developed because the earth is basi-cally a closed system with rather definite limits and capacities. The winds that ventilate the earth, for example, are only six miles high. There is a limit to the atmosphere—as vast as it may seem. That there is a limit to a river's ability to dilute wastes becomes obvious as toxic sewage and garbage gradually kill the tiny micro-organisms that normally clean the river. The sea is immense, and this apparent vastness has led man to turn to the sea as a useful, convenient, passive sink. But it, too, has limits; and although we have not exceeded its capacity, we do not know the irreversible changes that have been started by the harmful practices of centuries.

One way of viewing the problem of disposal is that we really consume nothing. We merely use things. We may burn, bury, grind, or flush our wastes away, but some sort of residue survives. In fact, modern technology insures that some of our wastes and

residues are almost impossible to do away with; for example,
the tin can that rusted away has been replaced by aluminum,
which is practically immortal and can withstand the ravages of
time and oxidation. The plastic container is another of the "im-
mortals" created by technology.

The problem of waste disposal is compounded because we are
surrounded by delicate balances that interlock. We live, for example, in an atmosphere that is a mixture of oxygen, nitrogen,
carbon dioxide, and water vapor. This mix is maintained by
plants, animals, and bacteria, which use and return the gases—
especially oxygen—at equal rates. The interlocking relationships
become apparent when you realize that 70 percent of the oxygen
found in the atmosphere is produced by ocean phytoplankton—
passively floating plants. Thus the ocean plays a significant role
in the balance of atmospheric oxygen. Delicate chemical relationships in ocean water also allow it to hold carbon dioxide
and to participate in maintaining a proper carbon dioxide balance
in the atmosphere.

We have polluted our atmosphere, and we have polluted our
streams, lakes, and rivers. We are also on the way to polluting
our oceans. But because of the interlocking nature of the balances, we will be in serious trouble if we succeed in polluting
the sea. A severe disturbance in plant, animal, and chemical
balances in the ocean will adversely affect the amount of oxygen
present in the atmosphere. And a decline in the oxygen supply
would mean a crisis for man. A change in the chemistry of
ocean waters that affects the carbon dioxide levels of the atmosphere would also be dangerous. Greatly raised levels of
carbon dioxide in the atmosphere might prevent heat from escaping into space. This would produce a hotter earth that would
melt the polar icecaps and raise ocean waters as much as
four hundred feet. A decrease in carbon dioxide levels of the
atmosphere, on the other hand, would also produce disastrous
effects. In a real sense, we live on a teeter-totter that is delicately
balanced.

No one needs to be told that the world is getting noisier.
Noise plagues our cities, and each of us accepts it as a constant
companion. Our willingness to tolerate noise and noisemakers is
related to our notion that noise is an intimate, inevitable part

A loudspeaker fills the neighborhood with its blare, adding a share of noise to the city.

of technological progress. The sounds produced by airplanes, automobiles, buses, trucks, power boats, power mowers, air hammers, bulldozers, chain saws, and industrial activity are accepted as an unavoidable price we must pay for a machine civilization.

But we are beginning to recognize that noise is a form of pollution that produces many harmful effects psychologically, physically, and emotionally. The problem is attracting more attention now than at any time in the past. And we are only beginning to recognize that we can control and reduce most of the noises that invade our environment.

Although the noise problem has been widely discussed, it has not yet been attacked in a thoroughgoing way. Most of the studies made have been to determine how much noise a worker can stand or tolerate. This is important, but our prime concern should be that noise produced by most or all sources constitutes an invasion of a person's right not to be disturbed. Once we assert this principle of personal privacy and the right to safety from noise, we will then begin to find ways to control and reduce the problem of noise pollution. The noisy industries themselves will begin to take steps to reduce the noise unleashed on workers and on people in the environment. This will especially be true if noise levels are controlled by law.

As a result of man's wanton pollution of his environment, there are numerous issues that must be faced and for which solutions must be found. We are bringing about a crisis in the natural environment because, in the past, we have been unable and unwilling to face and predict the biological consequences of our shameful practices. And today we are not much better at this task of facing reality. In fact, we blunder into the hazards before we are aware of them. We must somehow recognize the hazards in advance and bring to bear the social and political processes necessary to effect solutions before tragedy takes hold.

We are fond of saying that we control nature. This is a distortion of what really occurs. Man has, in fact, behaved as a very disorderly force; and his actions—the consequences of which he has not understood—have, for the most part, disrupted the scheme of nature. The truth is that man has produced a great deal of environmental modification but, as yet, no significant control; and the modifications that have been brought about have often misfired.

What is called for in the world today is a widespread awakening to the fact that the spacious skies of blue speckled with white clouds and beautiful sunrises and sunsets might soon be something that you can see only in a museum, painted by an artist of long ago. Dirty air, filthy streets, polluted rivers, lakes choked with debris, and ocean beaches covered with oil are much more common sights. Man has developed an enormous competence to interfere with the natural environment. He can spray insecticides, change the course of rivers, build huge dams, and unleash millions of automobiles and trucks; but what is more important is whether he can understand the natural environment and begin to live in harmony with it. There is serious doubt as to man's willingness to use his intelligence and the power of science to turn from the path of catastrophe.

Chapter 2

DISORDER AND DISRUPTION

During 1968, a campaign was launched in Borneo to rid a village of flies. The huge fly populations were not only bothersome, but they were suspected of contributing to the spread of disease among the rural people. The health officials decided to use DDT. This pesticide did the job efficiently and quickly. The fly population was destroyed, and the application of DDT was hailed as being effective.

When you look beyond the mere destruction of the flies, however, you find that this solution set off a chain of events that threatened the area with catastrophe. Lizards ordinarily feed on flies. After the application of the pesticide, the lizards who ate the flies accumulated the DDT in their bodies. Cats in the region feed on rats as well as lizards. Those cats who hunted and ate lizards, died. As the cat population decreased, the rat population increased and threatened the entire region with the spread of plague.

Plants, animals, and the physical environment are related and intertwined in what scientists call the *balance of nature*. When we introduce a chemical and try to use it selectively to destroy one animal, we often find that repercussions result from the disruption of the balance. When some residents of the environment are destroyed, others will prosper. The remaining plants and animals are really put in a state of disorder until a new balance is established. Each group undergoes a time of change and adjustment.

Let's agree that flies must go. But then once we agree, we must search for alternate solutions and we must study the possible consequences of each. We must not choose those solutions that will change the balance of nature and threaten man's

Each animal group is part of the balance of nature.

survival. We must learn to test the consequences of actions we plan in terms of the future of the world environment. An ill-conceived attack on an animal in Borneo, or in any other country, may set off a chain of events that will affect people around the world.

Man is driven by an insatiable desire to rid the world of insects. Admittedly, the cockroach, the Japanese beetle, and the corn earworm do not seem to have constructive roles in man's scheme of things. But insects are a part of a complex balance in nature that includes many other animals. Birds, for example, feed on insects. In the cold spring of 1967, birds migrating north faced difficult times and some starved to death because caterpillar hatching was delayed more than three weeks. Thus, whenever an insect is marked for destruction, we must ask:

• What means will be used to destroy the insect?
• What are the consequences of destroying the insect by this means?
• What other animals depend on this insect?
• What will happen to the balance in nature when this insect is removed or decreased in number?

The weapon man has used most "successfully" in his war on insects has been DDT. It has performed near-miracles in ridding much of the world of malaria, typhus, and other diseases. Another obvious benefit from the application of DDT is an increase in harvests when the insects that feed on the crops are destroyed.

Paul Mueller, the discoverer of DDT, won the Nobel Prize in Medicine and Physiology in 1948. The full name for DDT is *dichlorodiphenyltrichloroethane*. This organic chemical came into general use in the mid-1940s. It was the first of a big family of insecticides.

A Jeep is shown spreading insecticide just before sunset in a New Jersey coastal community. The pregnant mother and the child will be engulfed in the spray in another moment.

DDT is a solid that remains active for years. Winds, streams, rivers, and oceans can carry DDT far from the location where it is applied. Thus an animal in a distant place may absorb this chemical along with its water, nutrients, and food. As a result, DDT has accumulated and been concentrated in the cells of most animals. About twenty years after this insecticide first came into use, it was found that the average American's body contained ten to twelve parts per million (ppm) of DDT. The amount carried by humans is even higher in those parts of the world where massive use of the insecticide is employed for insect control in agriculture and in the control of the spread of malaria.

Experimental work, reported in 1969, indicated that DDT induces rats to produce abnormally large amounts of enzymes. These enzymes are turned out by the rat's liver as a defense against the DDT. But the enzymes also act against the body's own hormones—testosterone in males and estrogens in females. Since rats are a common laboratory substitute for man, and the same hormones are found in humans, it can be assumed that men and women are undergoing the same subtle changes that DDT induces in the rat. Similar findings about DDT have been reported in connection with quail, pigeons, and rabbits.

Another apparent effect of DDT is that its presence in the body causes unpredictable changes in the effects of some common drugs. The story of DDT and its use in the war on insects is far from written, but it seems probable that in the process of making war on insects man has also dealt himself a few blows that may prove quite damaging.

Animal life depends on a "food chain" in which some animals feed on plants, others hunt and feed on the plant eater, and still others hunt the hunters. The lower forms of life are usually devoured by higher forms, and so on up the ladder. Plankton, fishes, and eagles are part of such a food chain. This kind of chain magnifies the effects of a slight disturbance in the natural environment.

When DDT is sprayed across a field in low concentration to eradicate insects, we have the beginning of a slight disturbance in the natural balance. The DDT sprayed on fields, woods, and swamps makes its way into our streams, rivers, lakes,

An osprey is shown perched on an abandoned telegraph pole at Big Pine Key, Florida.

and oceans. The plankton-fish-eagle food chain magnifies the effect of DDT in the following way: Plankton in the sea use the minerals in the water to produce food through photosynthesis. In the process, the plankton accumulate the chemical DDT in their cells. Fish feeding on the plankton concentrate the insecticide in their bodies. Eagles are predators. They live at the edge of the sea and feed on fish. These birds swoop out of the sky, seize a fish, and devour it. An eagle that constantly feeds on fish containing DDT, in turn, builds a tremendous concentration of this chemical in its body. Thus the eagles fall accidental prey to man's use of DDT. They are, in a sense, innocent bystanders.

The U. S. Fish and Wildlife Service has been studying the effects of insecticides on the reproductive cycle of birds. Many scientists believe that chemical pesticides interfere with the bird's ability to reproduce. The eagle's egg-laying process is delayed, for example, as a result of the buildup of DDT in its body. In some cases, the DDT actually causes the bird to become sterile.

It is true that once a pesticide is introduced for sale to the public, its use is controlled by the government. There are rules for the number and strength of each application to each crop. There are also strong guidelines that regulate how DDT can be applied before a harvest. Then, after a harvest, "market basket" testing is undertaken to check on the amount of the chemical that remains on the processed and unprocessed foods.

Even though these safeguards have been taken with DDT, there has been a continuous buildup of its levels in the human body for the last twenty years. No one is quite sure what this means for the worldwide environment and for the human population of the world. But we do know that it has wreaked havoc among bird populations!

There is no argument with the fact that more than 93,500 different kinds of flying and crawling insects do great harm to our crops. Losses in the United States alone total billions of dollars annually. Thus there is a great temptation to weigh the good (increased food production and disease eradication) that a pesticide like DDT does, against the harm. But this is not our only choice. There are at least five other ways in which insects can be controlled.

• *Sterilization.* Mosquitoes, boll weevils, cockroaches, flies, aphids, and beetles have been sterilized with radioactive cobalt-60. This technique was especially successful in controlling the screwworm fly in Florida. This shiny blue-green fly lays its eggs in wounds on cattle. The eggs hatch into maggots that burrow into the cattle's flesh. Often, the animal is weakened and dies as a result of playing host to the maggots.

The technique worked this way with the screwworm: Millions of these insects were raised in captivity. They were fed a diet of hamburger and blood. Then the males were exposed to cobalt-60. The radiation sterilized the males. These male screwworms were able to mate with a female but were not able to fertilize her eggs. Millions of these sterilized males were released. So many of them mated with females throughout the Florida area that a good portion of the eggs laid did not hatch.

• *Insect traps.* The female carries a sex attractant or "perfume" that lures the male to her. This perfume can be used to bait traps to lure unsuspecting males. Once the males have been trapped, they can be destroyed, but it is much better to sterilize, infect with disease, and then release them to mate with females. The combination leaves the female eggs unfertilized, and she also contracts the disease carried by these males.

• *Natural enemies.* Each insect has natural enemies that hunt and destroy it. Ladybugs, for example, hunt and devour aphids. One way to combat the aphid is to encourage the ladybug by developing large numbers in captivity and releasing them in an area that suffers from aphid infestation.

• *Insect diseases.* Each insect has its own set of diseases to which it falls prey. Milky disease spores, for example, can be bought to infest and destroy the grubs of young Japanese beetles. The gypsy moth falls prey to a special Bacillus disease called *Bacillus thuringinesis.* This disease produces a crystal that is toxic to the caterpillars of the gypsy moth and the cabbage moth. The trick, of course, is to find diseases that kill certain insects and are harmless to man and other animals.

• *Starvation.* One very effective way of controlling insects is, of course, to cut off their food supply. This can be done by planting crops that are immune or resistant to the insect pest. Certain

The Hessian fly larva lives between the base of a leaf and the stem of the wheat plant and kills or so weakens the plant that no grain develops. Here is a field of wheat damaged by the Hessian fly.

varieties of wheat, for example, can be grown that are resistant to the Hessian fly. And there are corn varieties which are resistant to corn-loving insects.

There ought to be a sense of urgency in our study of these alternative ways to control insects. In 1970, for example, there were more than fifty pests that had developed an immunity to the pesticides. Michigan State University biologists, in 1968, produced flies that survived a drop of pure DDT. The dose used on each experimental fly was the equivalent of fourteen pounds of deadly poison given to a two-hundred-pound man. Through the course of normal evolution, we can expect fly populations and other insect populations to develop similar immunities to present insecticides. Then what do we do? Get ready to fight superfly!

As we explore the alternatives to DDT, we must ask in each case what the consequences of this new procedure for insect control will be. How will the balance that exists in the environment be disrupted by this new technique? In which directions can we reasonably expect the balance to shift? Will the shift in the balance, as a result of this disruption, be more beneficial to man?

Certainly it will cost time and money to develop new control procedures and to study the consequences of putting them into effect. If we do nothing, however, then we must recognize that the pesticides are the farmers' only protection. But the human race will be left unprotected in the long run even though our silos are full, because these chemicals remain on food and will eventually take their toll in biological changes induced in man. They kill birds, other wildlife, and the fish in our streams. And the worst condemnation of all is that they kill the useful insects too.

It seems that everywhere that man exists, he threatens the balance of nature. Man pours pollution into rivers and sky; he sprays pesticides indiscriminantly and pushes animal populations into oblivion. Some of the most flagrant destruction of animal life occurs in our streams, rivers, and lakes. An estimated 9,100,000 fish were killed by identifiable pollution sources in the continental United States alone during 1966. And, in fact, this was not the worst year. Almost twelve million fish were reported destroyed by pollution in 1965.

The overenrichment of water by wastes is one of the prime causes of fish fatalities. Lake Apopka, in Winter Garden, Florida, gives us an example of the way the natural environment of a lake can be disrupted to cause difficulty for fish. This lake receives effluents from the city's sewage treatment plant and citrus processing plant. There are farms in the surrounding area that use fertilizers and pesticides. The natural drainage from these farms carries some of the fertilizers and the pesticides into the lake. There are, of course, nutrients in all the wastes, from the citrus plant, the city sewage treatment plant, and from the farm drainage. The addition of these nutrients changes the delicate balance among the plants, animals, and the physical conditions within the lake. In fact, the nutrients pouring into the lake during July 1966 reduced the oxygen level to such an extent that fish could no longer survive. They literally suffocated to death. From this single disaster, more than one million fish were destroyed.

POLLUTION-CAUSED FISH KILL SUMMARY
(Confirmed Reports for 1966)

STATE OR DISTRICT	FISH KILLED
Alabama	1,072,513
Alaska	No report received
Arizona	66,400
˜Arkansas	1000
California	135,000
Colorado	No report received
Connecticut	5400
Delaware	No report received
District of Columbia	500,000
Florida	1,000,000
Georgia	10,000
Hawaii	20,070
Idaho	565,000
Illinois	808,730
Indiana	53,258
Iowa	21,250
Kansas	1,144,500
Kentucky	204,800
Louisiana	37,100
Maine	5000
Maryland	No report received
Massachusetts	1500
Michigan	7599
Minnesota	250
Mississippi	5030
Missouri	148,600
Montana	11,000
Nebraska	14,480
Nevada	1500
New Hampshire	13,000
New Jersey	22,897
New Mexico	No report received
New York	28,474
North Carolina	23,800
North Dakota	No report received
Ohio	764,570
Oklahoma	530
Oregon	19,600

Pennsylvania	1,493,819
Rhode Island	17,000
South Carolina	11,500
South Dakota	8000
Tennessee	13,375
Texas	167,250
Utah	No report received
Vermont	No report received
Virginia	15,694
Washington	14,500
West Virginia	234,915
Wisconsin	2750
Wyoming	51,000

MAJOR POLLUTION-CAUSED FISH KILLS—100,000 OR MORE
Confirmed for 1966

LAKE OR STREAM	NEAR OR IN	NUMBER KILLED	POLLUTION SOURCE
Lake Apopka	Winter Garden, Florida	1,000,000	Food products
Allegheny River	Sharpsburg, Pennsylvania	1,000,000	Mining
Valley Creek	Bessemer, Alabama	728,498	Food products
Anacostia River	District of Columbia	500,000	Sewage disposal
Snake River	Burley, Idaho	500,000	Food products
Kaskaskia River	Bondville, Illinois	370,653	Food products
Great Miami River	Butler County, Ohio	319,130	Chemical
Cottonwood and Neosho Rivers	Emporia, Kansas	300,000	Manure drainage
Cottonwood River Neosho Tributary	Emporia, Kansas	300,000	Manure drainage
Vermilion River	Danville, Illinois	291,181	Sewage disposal
Ohio River	Louisville, Kentucky	200,000	Chemicals
Big Kettle Creek	Cross Fort, Pennsylvania	195,642	Unknown
Coal River-Pond Fort	Van, West Virginia	180,000	Mining
Portage River	Ottawa County, Ohio	137,092	Industrial
Big Muddy River	Royalton, Illinois	104,091	Mining
Kings River	Sanger, California	102,134	Sewage disposal
Little Conewago Creek	Thomasville, Pennsylvania	101,382	Petroleum
Cottonwood River	Cedar Point, Kansas	100,000	Manure drainage
Neosho River Grand River Tributary	Emporia, Kansas	100,000	Unknown
Colorado River	Matagorda, Texas	100,000	Poisons

Coal mining operations in Pennsylvania produce tremendous amounts of materials excavated from the earth. A good portion of this material is waste, and it is usually placed in huge piles close to the mine. These waste deposits are acid in character and are referred to as *culm*. A culm pile is a gray-black mixture of slate, shale, sandstone, and the tailings of coal. Heavy rains occurred along the Allegheny River watershed during August 1966 and leached acid out of huge culm deposits in the area. The acid materials ran into the Allegheny River, turning it pea-green within a matter of hours. The bottom of the river near Sharpsburg, Pennsylvania, was covered with a white film. These pollutants caused the death of more than one million fish in the Sharpsburg area. The destruction of fish is a very dramatic indication that something has gone wrong and that the physical conditions in the water have changed drastically within a very short time. There are, of course, more subtle daily changes that go undetected and about which we do nothing.

HISTORICAL SUMMARY OF POLLUTION-CAUSED FISH KILLS
June 1960–December 1967

	June–December 1960	1961
Number of states reporting	36	45
Number of reports	286	411
Reports that specify number of fish killed	149	263
Total estimated number of fish killed	6,379,000	15,910,000
Average size of kill	2925	6535
Largest kill reported	5,000,000	5,387,000

1962	1963	1964	1965	1966	1967
37	37	40	44	46	40
381	381	485	531	436	375
233	300	385	446	372	303
7,118,000	7,860,000	18,387,000	11,784,000	9,115,000	11,591,000
5710	7775	5490	4310	5620	6460
3,180,000	2,000,000	7,887,000	3,000,000	1,000,000	6,549,000

Industrial waste was the single largest killer of fish in our streams, rivers, and lakes during 1966. More than 4,600,000 fish died as a result of this type of pollution. The waste produced in the manufacture and processing of food products is considered industrial in origin. Idaho, famous for its potatoes, gives us one of the worst examples of pollution resulting from the processing of food. Organic wastes from a potato processing plant were consistently dumped into Idaho's Snake River until the accumulation reduced the level of dissolved oxygen along a seven-mile stretch and suffocated five hundred thousand fish.

Government is the offender in many pollution cases. City waste, in fact, is the second largest killer of fish. During 1966, more than 1,300,000 fish died because of malfunctioning or inadequate municipal sewage treatment plants. City officials are negligent when they do not insist on proper maintenance checks and when they do not anticipate and plan for the needed capacities in municipal sewage treatment plants. Maintenance is particularly important because numerous difficulties can develop that allow raw sewage to enter the streams, as, for example, when a blower system breakdown in Danville, Illinois, in 1966 allowed raw sewage to pass into the Vermilion River and kill almost three hundred thousand fish.

The city is a public body. It seems that this status requires that it exercise special care. In too many cases, however, city officials have pointed accusing fingers at industry while they themselves have assumed immunity from responsibility and a license to pollute and destroy. It bears repeating: *In 1966, waste from cities was the second most deadly source of pollutants entering our streams, lakes, and rivers.*

Agriculture, too, contributes to the pollution that causes fish to die. The use of fertilizers and pesticides in 1966 alone resulted in the destruction of more than 1,200,000 fish. Even the fattening of animals for market can be potentially dangerous when drainage from special feed lots finds its way into our streams.

Transportation accidents, such as a pipeline springing a leak or a railroad car overturning, were responsible for the killing of more than one hundred thousand fish in 1966. This type of accident will occur, and there is some excuse for it. But it is inexcusable and the worst kind of negligence that some leaks go undetected for several days or longer. Such wanton negligence occurred at a creek crossing when a crude oil line was allowed to leak for several days, and fish were destroyed along a two-mile section of the stream.

Pollution in a Wisconsin lake killed these fish.

Other activities can only be classified as completely illegal, as, for example, the disposal of wastes at housing, industrial-plant, and highway-construction sites and the deliberate disposal of poisons by dumping them into water. If this seems to be an inconsequential matter, you should realize that more than 1,400,000 fish were destroyed by pollution resulting from highway construction and illegal disposal of poisons in 1966 alone. Some construction companies were cited for pouring excess cement at building and highway sites into rivers rather than into settling ponds. It is a matter of record that two million gallons of phenols were discharged into a bay when a heat exchanger extraction unit failed. On another occasion, a hot effluent with a high acid balance was discharged from a phosphate fertilizer plant. There is no excuse for such action. The people and the companies involved show a genuine contempt for the environment and are completely irresponsible.

It is worth repeating: The destruction of fish in streams and rivers is only the dramatic evidence that indicates that conditions have changed sufficiently to cause disaster. The insidious changes that take place day by day from small amounts of pollutants entering these waters go undetected. These small, daily changes, however, are as serious for the life of the river as the instant, quick-kill poisoning of fish.

Each of us *must* assume responsibility for the environment. We ought to be concerned about industrial pollution, and we should insist that something be done about it. But as we require industries to do something about their pollution, we must also ask the citizens of every township and city to look into the way wastes are disposed of in their own community, especially from their sewage facilities. Each community must accept responsibility for its own actions and the actions of the farmer and of the industrialist within its borders.

As a community and as a nation, we have the right to ask and insist on the individual assuming responsibility for his environment and that he be held responsible for his individual actions. If there is a breach of that responsibility because of ignorance, then we ought to ask that citizen to become informed as to the kinds of activities that lead to pollution and that disrupt the natural balance in the environment. And it is conceivable that people pollute out of ignorance, as, for example, in the case of a farmer, during 1966, who disposed of spoiled baled hay by dumping it into a stream. The oxygen deficiency that resulted from the decomposed organic matter caused two thousand fish to be killed in that stream. This farmer was poorly informed. Ignorance can be excused once. The second time we have a right to be appalled and to take action to protect ourselves and the environment.

Spongelike algae are shown decomposing on a Lake Ontario shoreline at Nine Mile Point, west of Oswego, New York.

Chapter 3

SYSTEMS UNDER STRESS

The Great Lakes region, the Everglades, and the Amazon area are examples of great systems of water, land, and living things. One hundred years ago, a journey across the Great Lakes or a trip into the Everglades was an experience filled with the unexpected and the anticipation of danger. Today the Amazon region still requires courage and the spirit of adventure to move into and across its great expanses.

Brave men discovered and then ventured out onto the Great Lakes. The early explorers and settlers of the Northwest Territory used the Great Lakes as their chief route of travel. Gradually the life and economy surrounding these lakes has changed, until today the region is one of the most important industrial areas of the United States. So, too, have the life and economy of the Everglades changed. And the plans for the Amazon will most certainly affect all in that region. The changes in the Great Lakes region and in the Everglades have been accompanied by tremendous error and a willful neglect of the natural balances that existed. The same mistakes may more than likely be repeated in the Amazon.

The five large, fresh water bodies, the Great Lakes, discovered by Samuel de Champlain in 1615, dominate the north central section of the United States. These lakes—Superior, Michigan, Huron, Erie, and Ontario—are connected with each other. The major overflow from them moves by way of the St. Lawrence River into the Gulf of St. Lawrence. A portion of the outflowing water, however, passes into the Mississippi River through the Chicago Drainage Canal and the Chicago River. The course of the Chicago River was turned away from Lake Michigan in 1900.

The surface water in Lake Superior stands at an elevation of

The Great Lakes.

602 feet above sea level. Each of the other lakes to the east has a lower elevation. Thus, as the water moves from its maximum elevation in the lakes to the sea, it descends more than six hundred feet. The greatest single drop of 326 feet occurs at Niagara Falls between Lake Erie and Lake Ontario.

Lake Superior is the largest fresh water lake in the world, covering a greater area than the state of South Carolina. Superior and three of the other four lakes form part of the natural boundary between the United States and Canada. The combined area of the Great Lakes is more than the total for the six states of New England. Lake Ontario, which is the smallest, is almost as large as New Jersey.

LAKE	AREA (sq. miles)	ELEVATION OF SURFACE (ft. above sea level)	GREATEST DEPTH (ft. from surface to bottom)
Superior	31,820	602	1333
Michigan	22,400	580	923
Huron	23,000	580	750
Erie	9940	572	210
Ontario	7540	246	802

In the 1700s, these lakes were beautifully blue and contained tremendous fish populations. With the buildup of the region, the lakes attained vast commercial importance; and this commercialism was so irresponsible that its result was the fouling and gradual destruction of these natural wonders. Stinking water, algae, debris, and filth are part of what was once a healthy, well-balanced environment for plants and animals.

Lake Erie is the shallowest of these lakes. It is also the filthiest. The Cuyahoga River, which moves through Cleveland into Lake Erie, carries a load of sewage, detergents, and chemicals into the lake each day. Today there are hardly any fish left in this lake. The organic content of Lake Erie is staggering. Overwhelming sewage pouring in from Detroit and other cities saps the oxygen from the water. The rapid accumulation of these wastes has sent the central portion of the lake to a zero oxygen level. Lake Erie's life cycle is under stress, and it is so out of balance that we can truly say that the lake is dying. Today it is a rank, muddy sink.

Urgent action is needed if Lake Erie is to be rescued from death. The other four lakes, however, are also in need of a massive cleanup and prevention campaign if they are to be saved. Renovation of the Great Lakes, if the task had been started before 1970, would have cost fifteen billion dollars. Each year the job is left undone adds to the cost. If the task is not undertaken within a reasonable time, no amount of money will give us the natural lake environment that flourished in the past.

The existence of many small communities around Lake Erie increases the difficulty of remedying its polluted state. The lake environment is, after all, not that of the water alone, nor does it simply include one or two miles of land surrounding the water. It is, in fact, composed of the land, water, plants, and animals of a rather large region. The only present possibility that might succeed is massive aid from both the United States and Canada and the establishment of a comprehensive governmental structure such as a Lake Erie Authority. A clear-cut jurisdiction is needed over the entire water system and surrounding area. Individual communities cannot be depended upon to take the necessary action to maintain a healthy environment.

The process that Lake Erie is undergoing is called *eutrophica-*

tion. This means that its waters are so filled with fertilizers and organic waste material that the entire character of the plant and animal population has changed. The water close to the surface is filled with plankton. This condition prevents light from reaching the deeper water levels, and any plants that survive there do not undergo photosynthesis, nor do they produce oxygen. If deep water plants exist at all, they use up the dissolved oxygen in the water for their own respiration. Thus, as a result of decreasing oxygen levels in the lake, most plants and animals die and decompose. The only organisms that survive in such an environment are those that can exist on a very low oxygen supply.

The problem with Lake Erie is, of course, not the fault of the lake itself. It is caused by the people in the surrounding communities. For the three hundred years during which environment developers have inhabited the shores around Lake Erie, there has been no large-scale social conscience or awareness of what a healthy environment means. Rather than living in harmony with nature, the communities around these lakes have produced stresses in the natural environment that have finally caused widespread change. It is only now, with catastrophe at our door, that we realize the damage that has been done. The Great Lakes, after all, contain one-half of the world's fresh water supply. Let that fact sink in and you will recognize the dimensions of the tragedy that has allowed these lakes to become foul and polluted.

The United States government established a Lake Survey Operation as part of the Army Corps of Engineers by an Act of Congress on March 3, 1841. This agency has charted and studied the waters of the Great Lakes for about 130 years. Thus there is a great body of information available to us, including systematic studies of those factors of the environment that affect the lake levels and the river flows.

It is important to have good, reliable information about the water flowing into a lake via a connecting river. It is also essential to have accurate measures of actual lake levels. The combination of information is used to estimate the amount of water that will be drawn from the lake by rivers below it. Good water management depends upon good information about actual water flow as well as about any anticipated changes. If, for example, a river

Pollution flows from Cleveland Harbor into Lake Erie.

is to be deepened by dredging operations, its capacity will increase; and this increase, in turn, means that a greater volume of water will flow. Widening a river, or deepening its channel, actually will lower the level of an upstream lake. Such changes should never be made without adequate planning by an agency charged with the responsibility of determining the consequences of the action. We must have a watchdog group that is able to assess consequences and protect the public interest.

In the center of the picture, you can see a sludge-filled ship. The huge barge is being loaded with ore from the piles on the left bank of the canal, with nearby smokestacks belching pollution into the air. This photo was taken in the vicinity of Trenton, Michigan, where the Detroit River empties its waste into Lake Erie.

The Great Lakes stretch across a large section of the United States. The strategic location of these masses of water has an effect on climate and precipitation in other sections of the country. An air mass, for example, moving out of Canada may pass over the lakes, pick up moisture from them, and have its physical characteristics altered by these huge bodies of water. These lakes sitting astride the north-central section of our country are a great natural resource that must be preserved; but, in addition, they must be studied carefully so we can predict their effect on weather, climate, and the ecology of other regions. Specifically, we need further information and research into what causes low water levels, high water levels, and what the evaporation rates are under different conditions.

The Everglades is one of the largest swamp areas in the world. It covers more than five thousand square miles in the southern part of Florida. But it is a very special kind of swamp; in fact, you might think of the Everglades as a river with grass growing in it. In this sense, it is one of the widest rivers in the world.

The water of the Everglades drains into the Gulf of Mexico. During the summer there is actually more than sixty inches of rainfall, and the whole area is flooded. During the winter, the area dries out somewhat, and the water that is flowing moves mostly in the sloughs.

The Everglades are generally south of Lake Okeechobee. But there are arms of the Everglades that extend around the eastern and western sides of the lake. The main body of swamps, however, stretches southward from Lake Okeechobee for about a hundred miles to the tip of the Florida peninsula. The width of the swamps is, on the average, about forty miles. They merge into salt water marshes and mangrove swamps near the Bay of Florida and the Gulf of Mexico.

The northern and eastern sections of the Everglades are covered by saw grass. The saw grass is a sedge. It is really not a grass. Wax myrtles, willows, and palms grow on clumps of higher land called *tree islands,* or hammocks. The soils found in the Everglades are composed largely of muck, peat, and gray marl. The muck and peat develop primarily from the remains of decayed plant life.

The state of Florida began draining large areas of the Everglades in 1906. The rich muck made suitable land for agriculture. Drainage canals were built from Lake Okeechobee to the ocean. This diversion, however, has deprived the swamp of large volumes of water; and falling water levels have produced difficulties over the years. The dry muck, for example, is very susceptible to fire; and salt water creeps from the ocean into wells in the area. In addition, the decreasing volume of water has created a great disturbance in the natural balance of life in the swamp.

The Everglades is a natural refuge for a great number of living things that form a complex web of life. Alligators in the Everglades eat a fish called *gar*. The gar feeds on minnows, and the minnows eat mosquito larvae. Thus, you might say, the alligator is dependent upon the mosquito population. In addition, the minnows that feed on mosquito larvae are eaten by a fish called *bream*, which in turn are eaten by bass. Dragon flies also feed on adult mosquitoes, and the numerous heron and egrets eat the minnows. Thus you begin to see an interconnecting web among the animal life found in the Everglades.

Alligators are among the most interesting animals that live in the Everglades. A female alligator will pick out a dry spot and prepare her nest by piling vegetation about three feet high and four feet long. The alligator lays about fifty eggs and then covers these eggs with more vegetation. The heat from the decaying vegetation incubates the eggs until the young alligators hatch. Most of the alligators that hatch are about eight inches long. Only 25 percent of the young alligators survive the first year. They grow eleven inches a year for the first seven years. After that point, growth is almost wholly dependent upon their diet.

The Everglades is a sprawling subtropical wilderness. A complex of young plant and animal communities exists in the wilderness. In recent years, however, man has intruded into this wilderness; and now it is being threatened with destruction. The drought, for example, that has existed in the Everglades during the last ten years has been mostly manmade. Land developers have been rushing in, draining, and building homes on the reclaimed land. They have been diverting water to drain the land. The huge volume being siphoned off from the natural flow causes water levels to drop, which, in turn, causes problems for

The baby alligator is sunning itself and resting.

the wildlife and produces fires. The developers are making a quick profit by building on land that is really not very suitable for housing.

There is no end to the disturbance caused in the natural environment because falling water levels and other man-produced conditions encourage the deposit of silt in some of the sloughs. Roadways are one of man's innovations that interfere with natural flow and natural processes in the swamp. A roadway put across a slough area acts as a dam. The water moving along the slough drops its silt when it runs into an obstacle. The silt can build to ten feet or more in such places. Then, in order to reestablish the natural state of things, dredges have to be moved in. Man is not always the culprit in such cases, however. Many times decayed vegetation causes damlike conditions in the slough, and silt builds behind it.

During the summer, the vegetation in the Everglades is very green. During the winter, it is all dried out and usually turns gray. Without sufficient fresh water, the wildlife and vegetation cannot reproduce. Rookeries, for example, form only when the water brings sufficient food, such as shrimp, fish, and crayfish for the birds to feast upon. Rookeries in the area are beset by dangers, but especially by drought.

The Miami area drainage system is a critical intrusion of man into the Everglades. The situation at the end of the 1960s was serious. It could become catastrophic in the next five to ten years, because the drainage canals alter the fresh water flow into the Everglades; and wildlife in the area depends upon a

The water in the mangrove swamp is very still. The swamp is a study in contrasts: reflections as well as dark and light areas make an interesting pattern. The unnerving silence of the swamp is broken periodically by the scream of a bird.

sufficient year-round flow of fresh water. Both plants and animals die under drought conditions, and fires flourish and burn
uncontrolled to ravage and desiccate the land.

There is a porous rock underlying southern Florida, *oolitic
limestone*. It holds a subterranean reservoir of fresh water. The
pressure from the sea keeps the fresh water from draining away.
The removal of great quantities of fresh water from this underground reserve by a growing population is also causing great
difficulties. In some locations, the depletion of the water in the
rocks causes areas to collapse. Big gaping sink holes dot the
countryside and become the reminders of man's interference
with nature's scheme.

The tropical waters of Florida Bay that surround the Everglades are a giant nursery for many kinds of life. These waters
are warmed by the sun, and food chains flourish. Birds eat fish,
big fish eat small fish, small fish eat copepods, and the copepods
eat the plankton. Within this vital food chain, each animal hunts
and is hunted. Decay enriches the bay so that life continues.
Man's intrusions into the Everglades may also have their repercussions in the waters of Florida Bay. It may be too late to control the unleashed forces and to correct the damage already
done. But we had better think it over, take another look, and
try harder.

The Amazon River extends across a large portion of the northern part of South America. This river has its beginnings in small
streams that form in the Andes Mountains. The Amazon River
Basin drains an area of about two and a half million square
miles. The estimated length of the Amazon is thirty-five hundred
miles. It flows into the Atlantic Ocean at the equator.

At a distance of about two thousand miles from the ocean, the
river's width is about one mile. As the Amazon approaches the
Atlantic Ocean, its width gradually changes. At one thousand
miles from the ocean, it is four miles wide. Its width continues
to increase until it is two hundred miles across where the river
meets the ocean. The estimates are that the Amazon River and
its tributaries have about thirty thousand miles of water surface
that are suitable for navigation.

During the rainy season the Amazon and the lower courses of
the larger tributaries overflow their banks. At these times, the

surrounding country takes on the appearance of a vast inland sea. Some of the most luxuriant vegetation on earth can be found in the Amazon Basin. Its dense forests are filled with an astounding assortment of plants and animals, and its waters are rich in fish. The Amazon Basin is known to contain valuable natural resources such as minerals and lumber. Large tracts of fertile land have never known the plow or the trod of man's foot. It is one of the few wild frontiers that remain in the world.

During 1968, there was a proposal that relatively inexpensive low dams be placed along this river system at strategic points. Nine dams have been suggested. These dams would serve to create a system of seven navigable lakes. One dam, more than twenty miles long, would be used to form an inland sea several times the size of Lake Superior.

This is certainly a very intriguing, daring plan. The lakes would create a vast transportation system. The interiors of Brazil, Argentina, Paraguay, Venezuela, Ecuador, Colombia, Peru, and Bolivia would be linked by this system. What a boon this would be for these countries! Or would it? Before we agree, let's stop for a moment to think. What will happen to the ecology of the region? What will happen to the delicate balances that exist in the plant and animal communities? What kinds of disturbances can be predicted? And the most crucial question of all: Will the benefits outweigh the disadvantages?

Then there is an overriding question: Will these changes in the Amazon area affect the rest of the world? What will the nature of the changes be? Some scientists predict that the added weight of water at the equator, that is, water retained by the series of nine dams, will add three seconds to the year, because the additional weight will cause the earth to rotate more slowly. And common sense tells us that this may not be the only change that occurs. There may, in fact, be rather widespread changes in daily weather as well as changes in climate. Do the advantages outweigh the risks?

The building of nine dams requires the relocation of at least one city, of about a hundred thousand people. At the present time, the Brazilian government has not embraced the scheme. But there is some thought that this "Great Lakes proposal" may be pushed at a later time.

Salvador is the capital of Bahia, the largest state in the northeast of Brazil. In the 1960s, only 52 percent of Salvador's 690,000 inhabitants had potable water services, supplied in limited quantity, with a resulting serious hygienic and health problem. The Inter-American Development Bank helped to finance a first-phase project to provide 85 percent of Salvador's population with potable water. As the Brazilian government looks to a grand plan for the Amazon Basin, it must also learn to think of some essential services that need to be provided for the people.

An agency named SUDAM (Superintendency for Amazon Development) was seeking to attract industry to the Amazon region during the latter part of the 1960s. More than 135 industrial projects—most of them in agriculture, lumber, textiles, food products, and minerals—have been started. There is a great temptation for industrialists to move into the Amazon region. Many incentives have been offered, and the lure of great profits seems irresistible.

The Amazon is a region that is unspoiled at the present moment. But it is a region with a rich potential, and it should be developed. The problem is to develop it in such a way that maximum benefits are brought to the people without destroying the region and the earth! It seems to me that a grand design and an extensive plan need to be developed to protect the natural environment and to avoid the pitfalls and mistakes that have led eventually to catastrophe in other regions.

One of the most obvious investment lures in the Amazon is lumber. Brazil has billions of acres of woodland in this area, with approximately twenty-five hundred kinds of hardwoods. Mahogany and rosewood, for example, are found in abundance in the Amazon Basin. The Georgia-Pacific Corporation moved into this region in the late 1960s. This company has produced huge harvests from timberland it owns in the region.

Another important resource, which more than likely will be exploited, is oil. When you realize that Brazil is one of the world's biggest petroleum importers, you can see some reason for exploration and exploitation of this natural resource if it is available in large quantities. Other minerals such as bauxite, copper, industrial diamonds, and gold also invite the speculator to move in to make his quick profit. Rubber, of course, was the source of the first fantastic boom in the Amazon fifty years ago.

The task for the development of the Amazon region will not be an easy one. Whether we have learned from mistakes made throughout the world and whether we will correct our procedures in opening the Amazon Basin remain to be seen. It will, of course, be tragic for the Amazon and the world if we repeat some of the blunders of the past.

Historically, we have been very slow to acknowledge difficulties and the actions that ought to be taken to correct them. The

United States, for example, did not officially recognize the need for a national wildlife refuge system until the beginning of the twentieth century. It was President Theodore Roosevelt who established the first national refuge on March 14, 1903 at Pelican Island on the east coast of Florida. By executive order, he set aside a five-acre area to protect the then favorite nesting site of the brown pelican.

There were state wildlife refuges that preceded the first national refuge. Lake Merritt in Oakland, California, was the first official state refuge established in North America. The state of California acted in 1870 to establish Lake Merritt as a sanctuary. Congress had established Yellowstone National Park in Wyoming before President Roosevelt's action; but Yellowstone was originally a recreational area, not a refuge. Prior to President Roosevelt's executive order, there was no official recognition that res-

A brown pelican floats lazily in the waters of Florida Bay.

ervations needed to be established for wildlife to preserve them from the intrusion of the city and from the developing industrial economy of the nation.

A wildlife refuge is defined as "an area of land or water set aside and managed for the protection and preservation of native plants and animals." Today there are almost three hundred national wildlife refuges. They cover a total of almost thirty million acres. I believe that national wildlife refuges are important and that the step taken by Theodore Roosevelt in 1903 was in the right direction. Today, however, we ought to recognize that refuges alone cannot solve the problem of restoring wildlife populations or, for that matter, even the problem of maintaining them. The Everglades, for example, is affected by changes that divert water and drain areas close to the "protected" section of the park. Stresses produced by these changes in turn create changes within the Everglades that disturb the animal populations. The problem is much broader than simply setting up an island or refuge in a turbulent sea of distress, overcrowding, and pollution.

The Migratory Bird Treaty Act ratified by many nations makes the conservation of such birds an obligation of national governments. The Duck Stamp Act in the United States requires every duck or goose hunter over the age of sixteen to buy a stamp each year. Ninety percent of the funds are used for maintaining refuges for migratory waterfowl. The areas set aside for these birds include breeding, fly-way, and wintering refuges. One of these refuges is at Pea Island, which is part of the Hatteras area in North Carolina. More than three hundred species of birds have been identified and recorded in the Cape Hatteras area. Snow geese winter here, as do Canada geese and many species of ducks. There are also large numbers of whistling swans, which spend the winter on the ponds in the area.

The fact that migratory birds are protected by the national governments points to the need for regional, national, and world-wide planning that takes into account the natural balances in nature. The Hatteras Island area of North Carolina, of which Cape Hatteras, at the southern tip of this island, is the most famous scenic area, illustrates regional planning undertaken by both state and federal governments. Hatteras Island lies over thirty miles east of the mainland across Pamlico Sound. The shoals are very dangerous, and over the centuries the many shipwrecks that have taken place in the area have earned it the name, "graveyard of the Atlantic." There are forty-five square miles of beach in this area. It is divided into four sections: Bodie, Hatteras, Ocracoke, and Pea Island National Wildlife Refuge. There are eight villages within the natural boundaries of this area. Each village is excluded from the national sea-shore, and there is ample room around each for expansion. Thus there is a balance in this area between recreational use and the preservation of plants, animals, and the shoreline.

Many wild flowers grow quite well in the humid climate of Hatteras. They blossom over a long growing season. There are,

Wild geese at Hatteras Island, North Carolina.

of course, other kinds of vegetation on the outer banks. There is mixed shrubbery of bayberry, silverling, youpon, and goulberry, as well as live oaks and loblolly pines. There are marsh grasses and the beach grasses that are used to stabilize the dunes. The sea, wind, and land contend with each other. Over the centuries there has been a pattern of never-ending change, but it is a change brought about by a seesaw in the balance of nature rather than the catastrophic change usually brought about by the intrusions of man.

The problem, of course, is to be alert to the need for utilizing land well and in harmony with nature. We can have industrial development, recreational areas, and the preservation of our wildlife. We can have a balance in nature that is beneficial to man. Let's not forget that man, after all, is part of nature. We can have all of this if we plan wisely and well, but this requires cooperation.

An example of such cooperation occurred in 1968, when a thirteen-hundred-acre marsh on the southern shore of Ontario, Canada, was preserved by an agreement between Bradley Farms, Ltd. of Chatham and the Canadian Department of Indian Affairs and Northern Development. Bradley Farms was to have drained and converted a marshland on its property into farmland. In 1968, a two-year agreement was signed with the owners of the marsh to study the problem, and an option was obtained to continue the agreement, if the two years of study indicated that the benefits of preserving the area were worth the cost. The marsh area has been a prime refuge for waterfowl, as well as a gathering point for migrating birds. Public interest, free enterprise, and the preservation of the natural balances in nature do not necessarily need to conflict. In my opinion, it is in the long-term interest of both the public and industry to nurture a proper regard for natural balances.

Wildlife refuges were an appropriate first step in 1903. But it seems that refuges alone are no longer sufficient. The concept needs to be extended to wider regional, national, and international planning that emphasizes proper use and preservation of the total environment. We, in fact, do not have much choice when we recognize that the earth, after all, has finite limits. We have gone much too far along the road with a reckless "to-hell-with-tomorrow attitude." We may have already set destructive forces in motion that cannot be stopped; and we may find that our environment is doomed to become unsuitable not only for wildlife but for man, too. Let's hope that there is time and that we have the determination to create and preserve a healthy, balanced environment.

The construction of the Aswan High Dam is shown in this general view of the downstream channel cofferdam. The Aswan High Dam was built to step up the economic development of the United Arab Republic and improve the welfare of its people. The Aswan power station generates ten billion kilowatt-hours a year; the newly irrigated lands yield thousands of tons of cotton, rice, and other crops.

Chapter 4

FOR THE WELFARE OF MAN

Look about and make a mental catalogue of the living things in your environment. And don't forget yourself! Man is one of more than one million different species of animals in existence today.

Although man is a part of this world of nature, he has behaved as if he were at war with the environment. In the past, he has torn down mountains, changed the course of rivers, drowned millions of acres of land with huge dams, raised the temperature of streams, cut trees for timber as rapidly as possible without adequate reforestation, and allowed an army, in Vietnam during the 1960s, to use herbicides to defoliate trees, shrubs, and crops. All these things and more have been done because someone thought they were in the national interest.

Each action we take has its consequences. Our desire for the benefits of the automobile and heavy industry has unleashed filth into the environment that is causing more than the throat and eye irritations from the Los Angeles smog and the stench from the unpleasant odors from Lake Erie. Pollution is, in fact, causing a drop in the temperature of the atmosphere by screening out solar radiation. The difference between today's median atmospheric temperature and that of the last ice age that occurred millions of years ago is only slightly more than seven degrees Fahrenheit. Not very much, is it? The frightening fact is that we have had a change of one degree Fahrenheit in the last twenty-five years as a result of man's negligence.

One suggested effect of this temperature change is that it is contributing to the migration of marine life. This fact becomes catastrophic when you realize that half the world's population depends on the animal proteins found in marine life. Marine animal migrations are resulting in a loss of food to impoverished peoples. And without this protein, infant mortality as well as mental retardation rates will climb.

In addition to migration we must also remember that pollution resulted in the concentration of DDT and other pesticides in marine life throughout the 1960s. The accumulation of DDT in plants and animals of the sea has produced some obvious defects among birds as a result of the way food chains work. And beyond the obvious effects produced in birds are those produced in man; these are not apparent, and we will become aware of them only in the future, when it is much too late to correct the situation.

A representative of the United States Department of Agriculture spent one month during 1968 in Vietnam studying the effect of the defoliation attacks. At that time, he indicated that the situation was not irreversible, but that it would take at least twenty years to fully restore some of the Vietnamese crops to what they had been before defoliation started. This means that in some cases normality will not be reached again before 1990.

Anything that changes one aspect of the physical environment or interrupts the life cycle of one plant or animal species may, in the long run, affect all of us. It may affect an individual dramatically within his own lifetime. Or, because a human lifetime is so fleeting, the individual may escape the full impact of the stress or change. If the changes are those that accumulate slowly, then evolutionary channels will certainly carry the drama along with the catastrophe to the individual's descendants.

In 1900, for example, engineers reversed the flow of the Chicago River, which had until that year emptied into Lake Michigan. Chicago's drinking water has always been drawn from the lake. The city officials of 1900 felt that the polluted condition of the river was endangering the water supply. Changing the course of the river momentarily saved the city's drinking water and Lake Michigan, but the action helped transform the Mississippi into a 2350-mile sewer. Over the last seventy years, all residents living along the Mississippi River have had the occasion to wrinkle their noses to fend off the stench from Chicago. In the long run, the diversion of the Chicago River did not prevent the pollution of Lake Michigan. The real problem—

This is a view of the Calumet River at Chicago, Illinois. We are looking
north. Steel plants can be seen on all sides (Republic Steel is at the right).
Hot outfalls from the plants cause the river water to steam, adding to the
clouds of smoke issuing from the plant chimneys.

one of waste disposal—was ignored. And today, Chicago, even
with its disposal plants, has not solved its problem of sewage.
During the summer of 1968, for example, a downpour overwhelmed Chicago's combined storm-and-sewer processing system
to send a twelve-mile-long slug of excrement into Lake Michigan.

There is a popular notion that the Germans are good organizers.
They have proven this to be the case by their actions in the
Ruhr Valley and its surrounding districts. Today the Ruhr River,

running through one of the most concentrated industrial areas of the world, is cleaner than it was fifty years ago. This is a real monument to German enterprise and organizational ability.

The Germans recognized that there is an interdependence of rivers, natural environment, communities of people, and industrial activity. Thus they thought of the Ruhr Valley not as an isolated entity but as a part of two other valleys and two other rivers: the Emscher and the Lippe. They believed and operated on the basis that events, or changes, in the Ruhr River and its valley ultimately would be reflected in the natural balance of the other valleys. They developed and are using today a district approach that plans for and coordinates activities in the three valleys.

The Germans have moved beyond city limits and even beyond a valleywide approach in their planning and control. Simply stated, it is an organizational plan, not a plan that depends on new technological advances. It is true that the Bayer Chemical plant at Leverkusen, outside Cologne, spent fifty million dollars to apply pollution control devices to all their processes; but the unique feature that makes things work in the valleys is the cooperation that exists between local governments and the industry in each area. It is a joint attack on pollution problems by industry and local government.

Cooperation has been established by getting all those responsible for polluting the area into an incorporated organization that is responsible for correcting the problem. This organization dates back to 1904, but it was reorganized under the Reich River Associations Act of 1937. Representatives of both industry and the municipalities act as a board of directors.

In the German scheme, each river has a mission. The Ruhr provides the district with drinking water, and a premium is placed on keeping this river clean. The Emscher and its tributaries are used to carry off the wastes from the districts. But these wastes are rendered harmless at treatment facilities built and maintained by the governing body before being placed in the Emscher. The Lippe River also provides the district with some drinking water, although its saline content is rather high. In recent years, ground water sources have been tapped to supplement the drinking water supplies for the district.

Germany has a long record of experience in the management of its natural resources. They have, for example, used their forests wisely and well for over a hundred years. And certainly throughout the twentieth century they have a history of close cooperation between government and industry in the preservation of the nation's resources. There is no real parallel for this kind of activity in the United States. But the fact remains that some kind of action is needed in the Americas. It can come from the initiative of industry itself, although we have very few examples of such enlightened initiative. In any event, action *must* be taken to halt and then reverse the trend of pollution and destruction of our environment. It would be a real sign of enlightened progress if the action results from the cooperative effort of municipalities, state governments, and industry.

The North American Water and Power Alliance (NAWAPA) is a plan that calls for the redistribution of the continent's surplus water to areas of need. In the late 1960s, this plan consisted of some preliminary engineering reports. Whether it ever comes to fruition will be determined by the ability of three countries (the United States, Canada, and Mexico) to work together cooperatively to solve the economic, engineering, and political problems involved in building a series of dams, canals, and power plants.

The distribution system of NAWAPA would serve and allocate water to provinces of Canada, thirty-five states of the United States, and three states in Mexico. The plan is to collect between 15 and 20 percent of the unused runoff waters of the North. This is water that now flows into the Bering Sea, the North Pacific, the Hudson Bay, and the Arctic Ocean. Thus, rather than allowing the water to escape, it is to be trapped and to become part of a common source along with water from the northwestern United States, from the Appalachian region, from the Great Lakes, and from other basins. Then, a continentwide bridging system is to be used to distribute the water.

Recognize that this plan calls for various basins in the United States to be interconnected. Before we can do this, we must push on with tremendous pollution abatement programs, or we will be transporting wastes from one basin to the other. Such a plan means that we need to put a stop to the use of water as a low-cost transporter of undertreated domestic and industrial wastes. Using our waterways as sewers ruins them for other users and costs too much when we want to restore their quality. The only way to stop this practice, however, is to take the profit out of irresponsible behavior, whether it is the behavior of an industrialist or a community.

This aerial view looks east over a portion of Lake Mead's Boulder Basin. We can see Fortification Mountain and the Black Mountain Range in the background. Lake Mead is backed up by the Bureau of Reclamation's Hoover Dam and, when full, is 115 miles long and covers 163,000 acres. Huge reservoirs cause the crust of the earth to be compacted.

The NAWAPA plan is bold and imaginative. It merits careful study to generate data that can be used to guide the policy of the three nations involved. It is safe to assume that NAWAPA, or some modification of it, is possible from an engineering standpoint. But there are major questions to be answered:

• This plan requires huge reservoirs. The storage capacity of the main reservoir would be equal to the volume of water in Lake Erie and would have a length of four hundred miles, an average width of ten miles, and an average depth of two hundred feet.

The weight of water in every large reservoir causes the crust of the earth to be compacted and sink. This is a slow but measurable process. The NAWAPA plan calls for the principal load of water to be placed along four hundred miles of the nine-hundred-mile Rocky Mountain Trench. A very careful study of the possible effects of the loading is needed.

• The NAWAPA plan will produce some changes in the natural balance of certain areas. The creation of reservoirs destroys plant life and brings about a redistribution of animal life. The migration routes of great herds of caribou, for example, would be disturbed, and a drastic change in the food supply available to all the animals in the vicinity of each reservoir would occur.

• There is the probability that some changes in climate will result from the implementation of this plan. One very obvious change is that large volumes of unfrozen water will be placed over permafrost areas of the North. More than likely, this will thaw the ground below. When this occurs, there may be a danger of landslides. But, in addition, the water will absorb and retain heat in a different way than the present ground cover.

What does this mean? No one is sure. But we had better have some good studies that suggest the possibilities and the alternatives before we commit ourselves and North America to vast and possibly irreversible changes. This we know: Whenever man undertakes a scheme so vast, there is sure to be a modification of nature. This plan, and others like it, must be studied carefully so that, as man acts for his own purposes of the moment, he will not commit future generations to the dismal prospects of chaos.

Man's search for minerals has taken him to distant parts of the world to satisfy his hunger. The Spanish explorers, searching for gold, probed the American continents during the fifteenth and sixteenth centuries. Some found their gold, but others searched in vain for El Dorado, a fictitious kingdom of enormous wealth. In the twentieth century, another mineral, oil, the "black gold" of today, leads man to hunt and brave all kinds of hazards.

An Aramco sand buggy transports an oil exploration team and its equipment across Saudi Arabia's Rub' al Khali (The Empty Quarter), a vast, sand dune-spotted desert covering approximately 250,000 square miles. The buggy's large, low-pressure tires give the vehicle high mobility in desert terrain.

The searing deserts of Saudi Arabia were probed in the 1930s by American oilmen. Their work was given a great priority during the 1940s. Our mechanized army of World War II required and consumed great amounts of oil. The Arabian fields close to the battlefields of Europe and Africa were of great strategic importance. Today, almost seven hundred million barrels of oil, each barrel equivalent to forty-two gallons, are taken each year from this desertland and fed into the commerce of the world.

Within the continental United States, almost three billion barrels of oil are withdrawn from the ground each year. This is a staggering amount of liquid material. But we manage to use it all to supply energy to our airplanes, trucks, automobiles, and to heat homes, offices, and industrial plants. The petroleum companies of the United States have an investment that approaches seventy billion dollars in property and machinery. More than 1½ million people earn their living by working in the petroleum industry.

There are more than thirty-one billion barrels of proved crude oil reserves in the United States. And herein lies a dilemma. We have huge energy requirements. Today, we are satisfying our hunger for energy by burning petroleum and its products, i.e., gasoline, kerosene, fuel oil, and jet fuel. There are obvious limits to the amount of crude oil that exists in the world. We do not manufacture it. We must search it out and remove it from the ground. Without further exploration and discovery of new crude oil reserves, we, in the United States, could run out of this source of energy in the next ten years. Recognize that we are currently using almost three billion barrels a year, and that our proved reserves only amount to some thirty-one billion barrels.

If we were to depend only on crude oil for energy, we would obviously be courting disaster. We, of course, have had other options for a long time. Energy can be generated by hydroelectric plants in which water from dams is used to turn generators to produce electric power. We have produced some energy by this means, but not enough. We also have recently turned to the use of natural gas by piping it from the fields to home and industry. This is an improvement over the former wasteful practice of simply burning off the natural gas at the wells.

The tragedy that runs through the story of our need for energy is that we have not turned more quickly to atomic energy. We have had this source available to us for the production of energy since the mid-1940s. A quarter of a century later, we had not really begun to tap this power source in a major way, even for the production of electrical energy. As mentioned earlier, if we were to start the conversion to atomic power today, it would be difficult to have more than 50 percent of our utility installations operating with nuclear power by the year 2000.

In the meantime, we are conducting frantic searches for new oil fields. During February 1968, a vast new field was discovered on the North Slope of Alaska. This area is a coastal plain that stretches fifty miles across the top of our forty-ninth state. Winter temperatures plunge to sixty-five degrees below zero Fahrenheit, and winds moving at fifty miles per hour whip off the Arctic Ocean. The North Slope is bleak, cold, isolated, flat, and, in the wintertime, always dark. But, it is only during the wintertime that the tundra freezes solid enough to support the weight of heavy equipment. The work to tap this vast underground reservoir of oil began in January 1969.

Some estimates indicate that the total amount of oil in the field could amount to forty billion barrels. This will, of course, bolster the U.S. petroleum reserves. The possibility is that our reserves have been at least doubled by this new find. The impact of this oil will be widespread and will reshape the world oil picture. It will probably delay, for up to fifteen years, the need to explore and exploit new fuels. This bonanza of new oil that we will exploit during the 1970s will only lengthen the road to an energy disaster unless we push our research, development, and actual use of atomic fuels. We have been very slow in utilizing fission fuels such as uranium and plutonium. And we have not put enough effort into the development of controlled fusion processes, which would open vast sources of power and energy. We have simply lacked the determination and the sense of urgency.

Beyond the pressing problem of man's need and constant search for energy, the burning of fossil fuels—i.e., oil, coal, and natural gas—has contributed to the worldwide problem of pollution. Waste gases from these fuels have added significant irritants and great amounts of carbon dioxide to the atmosphere. And the addition of carbon dioxide has done a great deal to alter the climate of the earth. No one knows quantitatively how great the alteration has been, but we know that it has occurred.

Not only is man's use of oil dangerous, but his search for it is hazardous too. Some of the difficulties result from the fact that we are probing into the crust of the earth—something we know very little about. The Marlin No. 1 rig, for example, was a massive offshore oil-drilling platform that loomed over the green waters of Bass Strait, twenty-four miles off Australia's southeast coast, in November 1968. This huge platform was anchored to the ocean floor two hundred feet below by sixteen spidery legs. One of its drills penetrated to a depth of four thousand feet, but accidentally it followed a natural fault line through the earth's crust and triggered a massive leak of natural gas. A high-pressure pocket began spewing gas out along the fault line. The force of the escaping gas tore huge craters in the ocean floor.

This accident endangered a field estimated to contain 3⅓ trillion cubic feet of natural gas. Invisible, but deadly, gas boiled to the surface and stirred the sea. The gas hung over the area as a huge, potential fireball. Stopping the leak literally meant mending a huge crack in the ocean floor.

There is no argument with the fact that we need energy for our mechanized society. To satisfy this need, we must admit that man has been imaginative and persevering in searching for, finding, and exploiting fossil fuels—especially oil. But we must also recognize that our exploitation of this fuel is depleting an irreplaceable resource. We have moved too far down the road to completely turn away from it. But we must begin to recognize the kinds of disaster we court by (1) our continued depletion of this resource at the present rate and (2) the burning of these fuels in furnaces, the internal combustion engine, the diesel engine, and the jet engine, which release pollutants into the atmosphere.

Too often, our actions are guided by the economic realities of the moment: Certainly an industry has an obligation to return a profit to its owners or shareholders. And every community must be run as economically as possible with as little burden on the taxpayer as possible. But there are overriding public interests that must be served, too; that is, we must preserve and maintain the environment so that it will support the development of man and his civilization. Not only at the present moment, but in the future too!

This is the way land looks when conventional phosphate mining has been completed. This area was mined in 1957, before the development of simultaneous mining and reclamation by American Cynamid Company. It is at Cynamid's Sydney Mine, a few miles east of Tampa.

Man is usually in trouble when the natural balances of the environment are destroyed. The movement toward new balances as a result of stress places plants and animals of that environment, as well as man, under the pressure of change. If the environment becomes so fouled and used so poorly that man

After reclamation, land mined for phosphate by American Cynamid Company looks like this. This tract at Cynamid's Sydney Mine in Hillsborough County was reclaimed in 1961 and 1962. For more than ten consecutive years, American Cynamid has reclaimed more land than it has mined.

can no longer comfortably exist, then we are in trouble.

The human community—call it town, city, county, or state—is responsible for most of the problems developing in the environment. It is also the only agent that can correct these same excesses and stresses. We are faced with a dilemma. The only way out is for the community to recognize its obligation to (1) identify problems, (2) stimulate the research needed to provide alternative solutions to the problems, and (3) stimulate the development of organizations that will select the most promising solutions and apply them to the resolution of the problems of environmental pollution.

In my opinion, the citizenry, through its community agencies, is responsible for initiating and stimulating positive action. The community is responsible for identifying and keeping the inventory of how problems are being and have been handled. There are two special sectors of every community whose support can be elicited, encouraged, and, if everything else fails, required: the industrial sector and academic sector.

The industrial sector can, of course, be required to participate in stemming and controlling their own pollution of the environment by law. I personally would prefer, however, that we examine the problem in a more enlightened way—a way in which the industrialist is considered a good member of society and is given an adequate opportunity to recognize his obligations.

Most industry in our country is owned by shareholders. Through our markets in stock, ownership is spread. As the saying goes, you can own your share of America through stock. Many of our industries compete not only for the markets in this country, but also in foreign countries. Industry has had a major share in building the strength of our nation. Therefore, as we "clean up our environment," we must not destroy the economic potential of our industry and destroy our nation in a different way. I personally prefer that during the 1970s we provide strong advantages to those industries that move quickly to curb and control their own pollution of the environment. We should offer tax advantages that allow a progressive, responsible industry to enjoy larger profits than one that is reluctant and takes minimum measures to combat pollution. In addition, I believe we should develop some modification of the Ruhr district scheme that can appropriately cope with the special problems of our economy and the much greater distances involved.

In the area of power development, I believe we need to re-think our goals. Utilities such as Commonwealth Edison, Phila-delphia Gas and Electric, Allegheny Power, and Tucson Gas and Electric are privately owned, but their rates are publicly controlled. There is a real need to stimulate a movement away from the burning of fossil fuels (coal and oil) to the use of atomic fuels. The use of atomic fuels is in the public interest.

A roof rat on the prowl in the United States.

When a utility wants to build a new installation, it must seek to borrow money. It pays interest on the money borrowed, often a high rate, especially during the latter part of the 1960s. The utilities should be given a greater incentive to convert to atomic power. They should be allowed to retain a higher percentage of profit from the sale of electricity generated by atomic power than from electricity generated by the burning of fossil fuels.

We have an excellent example of the way in which citizens, communities, and a nation fail to recognize their responsibilities in the off-again, on-again rat bills of 1967 and 1968. During 1967, the national administration requested forty million dollars of Congress to attack the rat problem faced by every town and city in the nation. No funds were appropriated in 1967, and the House of Representatives Appropriations Committee cut out all the money authorized for rat control in 1968.

Rats have flourished in this world for fifty million years, so the problem is not a new one. Rats nibble, gnaw, kill, squeak, and spread deadly diseases through community after community. The bubonic plague or Black Death of the Middle Ages reduced Europe's population by a quarter. A grim reminder of the ever-present threat of this plague came in February 1963, when a dead rat was found in San Francisco infected with a bubonic plague bacillus. Typhus is transmitted to man from the lice of rats. Amoebic dysentery, infectious jaundice, and rabies are other diseases spread by this rodent.

Today there is roughly one rat for every person in the world, i.e., 3.3 million of each. In some ways in the United States, we are very fortunate, since our rat population is estimated to be slightly more than ninety million. This means that there is only one rat for about every two people in this country. But our rat population is very active. It does more than nine hundred million dollars' worth of physical damage each year.

When will we recognize the seriousness of the rat problem? Any action to be successful must be maintained year after year, and it must have the wholehearted support of every citizen. If one family or one community is careless, some rats will have ideal conditions under which to live and reproduce. And the rat population will eventually spill over into the surrounding communities.

University scientists have a significant role to play in helping the communities of the world to maintain a healthy and well-balanced environment. Their role is primarily that of research to provide alternate solutions to problems communities are facing. As an example, let's take another look at man's problem with the insects. Most communities have begun to recognize that the spraying of DDT and other chemical pesticides can lead to stresses and changes in the natural environment that are not beneficial to man. In the search for alternate solutions, university scientists studied a juvenile hormone secreted by insects. They found that the hormone must be present at certain stages of an insect's life cycle to regulate growth and to control the change from larva to pupa. At other times, the hormone must be absent or the insect will develop abnormally.

This juvenile hormone can be synthesized or made by man in his chemical plants. If a sufficient dose of this chemical is given to a mature female, it can sterilize her for life. Now, it might occur to you that an easy solution would be to spray this hormone across a field and thus prevent future generations of insects from developing. But if this were done, it would eliminate all insects, both harmful and beneficial. And remember that there are beneficial insects. What would happen to our plants and natural environment if we were to eliminate the insects essential for pollination?

A team of Czechoslovak scientists in Prague working with biologist Karel Sláma developed a technique in 1968 for using hormonelike chemicals to attack one species of insect at a time. They used DMF, a synthesized chemical that acts like a juvenile hormone, to sterilize females. But they did it in this way: They treated male linden bugs with a massive quantity of DMF. When the males were allowed to mate with the females, it was found that enough DMF was passed on to the female to make her sterile. The DMF was passed on to the female through the male sexual fluids.

Male linden bugs treated with DMF and released in nature can be used to pass the DMF on to wild females. Then even if the sterilized female does mate with a normal male, at a later time, no offspring will be produced. Insects cannot develop an immunity to this chemical, because if they did they would become immune to the hormone that is essential to part of their life cycle.

DMF itself affects the sterility of only a few insect species. Thus, scientists, such as Harvard biologist Carroll Williams, are searching for juvenile hormonelike chemicals that can be used to sterilize a wide variety of insect pests. The technique affects only the treated species of insects. It does not contaminate plant and animal life.

Here, then, is an alternate solution with possible practical applications to a community problem. In the past, government grants have been given to university scientists to conduct research. In my opinion, this program of government grants of tax money to support basic research should be continued and expanded. And each citizen should be made aware of the benefits that result from this kind of support.

An international campaign was necessary to save the Nubian monuments in the United Arab Republic. These monuments were originally on land that is now flooded as a result of the construction of the Aswan High Dam. The campaign was launched by UNESCO in 1960 to reconstruct the Abu Simbel Great and Small Temples on new sites. The work was completed in September 1968. The temples are shown on their new sites.

This close-up of the Abu Simbel Great Temple being re-erected on its new site gives you some idea of the size of the task undertaken in this international campaign for the safeguard of the Nubian monuments.

This picture shows the actual re-erection of the Great Temple on its new site.

Chapter 5

POLLUTION OF THE ATMOSPHERE

"Air pollution" is an all-inclusive term. In the popular sense, it covers the entire scale of pollutants: smoke, dusts, mists, odors, and gases such as carbon monoxide and smog itself. It was not until the 1960s that air pollution began to be recognized as a serious national and international problem. This lack of recognition for the problem is amazing, since deaths from air pollution were officially registered as early as 1930, when sixty-three persons died from it in the heavily industrialized Meuse Valley of Belgium.

There was other evidence, too, that the atmosphere was being overtaxed; but there could be no doubt about the warning the skies delivered in October 1948 at the coal mining town of Donora, Pennsylvania. Clearly, the skies were poisoned beyond endurance; and twenty deaths occurred among the six thousand people who became ill. The fourteen thousand residents of Donora had a rough four days.

One of the worst tragedies of the 1950s was reported from London. A heavy toll of almost four thousand deaths was attributed to the five-day siege of pollutants mixed with fog that hovered over London in early December 1952. The effects lingered on long after the smog dispersed. Over the next two months, another eight thousand deaths were attributed to the killer smog.

During the next ten years, there was a mounting number of tragedies: New York in 1953, two hundred deaths; London in 1956, one thousand deaths; another London episode in 1962 claimed three hundred lives; New York was revisited in 1963, with a toll of four hundred deaths. Slowly air pollution became a worldwide preoccupation.

We need only look about to find the evidence of pollutants entering our atmosphere.

And finally there is hope! Why? Because the dimensions of the problem are recognized. Now we can push on to the next step—research and the *gathering of information* to develop possible alternate solutions to the problem—alternate solutions from which we can choose the best.

In the natural state, air should contain 78 percent nitrogen, 21 percent oxygen, and 1 percent of a combination of carbon dioxide and other gases usually referred to as inert. Normally, this mixture of gases is thought of as invisible, odorless, and tasteless. By the end of the 1960s, there was not much of this kind of air in industrialized areas. There were, in fact, large amounts of contaminants—pollutants—in the air.

The use of the word "pollutant" seems to imply that the mere presence of a material in the atmosphere makes the air less safe to use. This is not necessarily true. Salt and dust normally can occur in the atmosphere. These particles are not necessarily harmful contaminants. They are, in fact, essential. Water vapor in the air condenses and forms as raindrops around salt and dust particles. These contaminants, then, are essential to rainfall. When we talk about pollutants, we must be certain to identify the character of each and its chemical composition. We must also define what the effects of the contaminant are before we classify it as a harmful pollutant.

From one point of view you might say that plant life introduces contaminants: odors and pollen. Some ten million people in the United States suffer from hay fever. In the Northeast alone, some 250,000 tons of irritating pollen can be released when there is a bumper crop of ragweed watered by heavy spring rains. To those members of the population who are sensitive to pollen and suffer tickling throats, watering eyes, and dripping noses, this can be the worst form of pollutant present in the air. Those of us not sensitive to pollen will have no personal problems as a result of its presence.

Practically no one would want to do away with the delightful smell in the pine forest or the odor of a Christmas tree. The odor of pine results from a type of hydrocarbon called a *terpine,* which is emitted by the tree. These hydrocarbons form a haze when they react with sunlight. In fact, the Blue Ridge Mountains really do look blue from a distance as a result of the haze produced by the trees and sunlight.

The point to remember is that plants, animals, volcanoes, geysers, and other features of the environment do release and have been releasing contaminants over the ages. Thus clean air over the centuries has had many natural contaminants. These contaminants, however, were not a problem. The atmosphere was able to handle them. Realistically, we must make a distinction between *clean* air and *pure* air. Clean air is desirable; whereas pure air, a clinical mixture of oxygen and nitrogen, which is completely odorless, is not possible in the natural environment and is, in fact, undesirable.

Historically, there have been pivotal events that have produced pollution that has overwhelmed the atmosphere. By 1800, for example, many changes in methods of production had taken place. Handwork was replaced by machinery, and great factories were created. Smokestacks came on the scene, and by 1900 they had reached into the sky in all the industrializing countries of the world. During the nineteenth century increased amounts of industrial pollutants were added to the atmosphere, and this trend continued into the twentieth century. To the factory smoke-stack, the twentieth century added the automobile. The harm-ful pollutants poured into the atmosphere at increasing rates until we reached the disaster levels of the late 1960s.

The carbon monoxide levels reported in the late 1960s provide an excellent way of distinguishing between a natural contaminant in "clean" air and a harmful pollutant that makes air "dirty." The automobiles of the 1960s poured out significant amounts of carbon monoxide into the air. At a concentration of slightly more than 1000 parts per million (ppm), carbon monoxide kills quickly. Most people, however, experience dizziness and a head-ache at levels of 100 ppm. Concentrations as high as 72 ppm were observed consistently in Los Angeles. Detroit, at times, registered carbon monoxide concentrations above 100 ppm. In almost every metropolitan area of the United States during the 1960s, the concentration of carbon monoxide at peak traffic hours was approaching the 100-ppm level.

All animals depend on oxygen for survival. We take air into our lungs and extract oxygen from it. The oxygen is used in the animal body to oxidize food and supply energy. In the process, the oxygen is converted to carbon dioxide and water. These prod-ucts are considered wastes, and they are discharged into the atmosphere by the animal.

The carbon dioxide produced by animals and man is im-portant to plants. All green plants depend on it for survival and growth. Through the process of photosynthesis, green plants use energy from the sun to convert the carbon from carbon dioxide and the hydrogen from water into the chemical building blocks of sugars. During the food-making process oxygen is liberated. The oxygen released by plants moves back into the atmosphere and is then available for animals to use again.

Thus you might say that plants take an animal's waste products

Automobiles choke our streets.

and convert them into waste products that the animal can use. There is then an essential and enduring balance between the plants and the animals. Man, as one of the animals in the environment, benefits from this balance.

The automobile has been mentioned as a prime offender, since it adds harmful pollutants to the air. But, in truth, the pollutants are not the inevitable result of the gasoline engine's combustion process. If one pound of gasoline and fifteen pounds of air are mixed together in the right environment, the chemical reaction that takes place will give energy and two other products: carbon dioxide and water. These wastes, carbon dioxide and water, are essentially those produced by animal life in generating its energy. Thus, if an automobile engine were to use gasoline under ideal conditions, we might have the simple wastes that plants could handle and convert to useful oxygen and food.

The problem, however, is that today's automobile engines do not operate to give an ideal chemical reaction. The fault is not with the engine; it is with people. They have not been interested in having the automobile engine carry out an ideal chemical reaction. Rather, most automobile owners want to drive down a highway as fast as possible, move up and down a hill with good response, and they want the engine to idle, accelerate, and respond to every touch of the accelerator. Over the years, engineers have determined that the simplest, lowest-cost way of providing the engine performance people expect is to supply a little more fuel than is necessary for ideal combustion conditions. As a result of this extra fuel, the combustion process produces carbon monoxide and a variety of hydrocarbons.

The automobile of the 1960s operated at very high temperatures. At peak engine temperatures, nitric oxide is formed by the reaction of oxygen in the air with nitrogen in the air. The heat of the automobile engine brings this reaction about. The pollutant added to the air as a result of the high operating temperatures has, in fact, nothing to do with the fuel.

There are at least three ways of solving the problem of pollutants emitted by the internal combustion engine:

• *Exhaust control.* Automobile exhaust control devices can prevent significant amounts of pollutants from escaping into the air. None of the control devices developed and applied in the late

1960s, however, controlled all of the poisonous gases emitted. Under the 1960 standards, tailpipe emissions from gasoline-fueled passenger cars and light trucks is limited to twenty-three grams of carbon monoxide and 2.2 grams of hydrocarbons for each mile of driving. But even under these standards, an estimated eight million pounds of carbon monoxide, one million pounds of hydrocarbons, and two hundred thousand pounds of nitric oxide are poured out on New York City streets each day.

• *Redesign the internal combustion engine.* In the long run, this

This is an experimental electric automobile built by the General Electric Company.

is probably the least costly and most durable way to solve the problem. The redesign should eliminate the need for extra fuel under any operating condition and reduce the peak operating temperature without affecting the combustion process. This is not the easy route, and it does require evolving some completely new approaches to the internal combustion engine.

• *Use electric cars.* The electric automobile is a possibility. Satisfactory technology for short-distance, electrically powered vehicles was available in the late 1960s. The use of the electric car in New York City as taxicabs would drop the hydrocarbon and carbon monoxide levels significantly. The taxis of New York City account for about 50 percent of all mileage driven within the city. Most city driving is done in highly congested areas. There is no need for large engines capable of developing tremendous power and speeds. The electric taxicab could be developed for cities in the 1970s. It will be if the citizenry insists!

Coal, natural gas, and heavy fuel oil are burned to supply the energy needs of the nation. Nationally, coal, throughout the period of the 1960s, supplied more than half the commercial and industrial needs for energy. Natural gas was the second most popular fuel, and oil was the third. If you were to examine certain areas, however, such as the New York-New Jersey metropolitan complex, you would have found oil to be the most popular fuel.

The bulk of heavy fuel oil and coal used in the United States contains sulphur as an impurity. And when the fuel is burned, the sulphur burns too. Sulphur combines with oxygen in the process of burning and forms sulphur dioxide. A small but measureable amount of sulphur trioxide is also produced, and it is converted immediately to sulphuric acid by the moisture in the atmosphere.

Sulphur dioxide can be absorbed by solid particles in the air and can be carried deep into the lungs to injure delicate tissues. The presence of any amount of sulphur dioxide gas in the air is quite noticeable, since it irritates the upper respiratory tract. Sulphuric acid is particularly damaging to tissue. Medical reports indicate that certain portions of the population are very vulnerable to sulphur pollution of the atmosphere. Heart and respiratory difficulties have been attributed to this pollutant.

Under most conditions, the burning of fossil fuels also produces soot and small particles of ash. These pollutants are referred to as particulate matter. There are a great variety of mechanical and electrical devices that can remove these pollutants from the flue gases. In fact, 99 percent of the soot and ash can be removed in the chimney area.

There are a number of options available to decrease the amount of sulphur pollutants in the atmosphere:

The pollution in the St. Louis area has, at times, been unbelievable.

- Convert coal to a liquid, gaseous, or modified solid fuel to reduce its sulphur content.
- Take the sulphur out of the fuel oil at the refinery.
- Only use oils and coals with low sulphur content.
- Change to other fuels (natural gas or nuclear energy).

Action is needed. Recognize that the oxides of sulphur are the second largest component of air pollution after carbon monoxide. These two (carbon monoxide and oxides of sulphur) account for approximately 80 percent, by weight, of all the harmful pollutants spreading through the air of our country. In some ways, carbon monoxide will be easier to control and reduce in the 1970s. The sulphur oxides spew forth from private homes, apartment houses, power plants, and factories. It was estimated that more than thirty million tons of sulphur oxides were released into the nation's atmosphere during 1968. By 1980, sixty million tons of sulphur oxides will be released during that year unless effective control methods are used on a wide scale.

Pollutants are produced by almost every important manufacturing process. Pulp and paper mills, iron and steel mills, petroleum refineries, smelters, inorganic chemical manufacturers (fertilizers, among others), and organic chemical manufacturers such as producers of synthetic rubber constitute only a partial list.

Particularly foul odors are associated with many processes: resin manufacturing, paint and varnish production, metal decorating, wire enameling, printing, potato chip drying, and rendering of animal fats. With almost no exceptions, the fumes streaming into the sky from industrial plants engaged in these processes contain pollutant gases. A wide range of these odorous air pollutants can be effectively destroyed by incineration methods. To clean up such exhaust gases, it is necessary to heat them to temperatures in the 1200–1500° F range. Another technique that can be employed is to use catalysts to promote oxidation at a lower temperature range of 700–900° F.

The burning of paper, grass, garbage, and leaves in 1969 dumped about six million tons of pollutants into the atmosphere. The fragrant custom of burning fall leaves is an enormous source of air pollution. The smoke that smells so good consists of ash and half-burned particles that are really dangerous litter. The falling leaves of autumn should be hauled away by a municipal or township authority. They should be burned only at an incineration plant that has proper stack control to prevent pollutants from belching into the air. If sufficient space is available, some of the leaves can be retained in a compost pile that can be used to good advantage in building up soil quality.

Asbestosis is a lung ailment that seriously impairs a person's ability to breathe. Physicians treating one asbestosis victim attributed his breathing difficulties and his development of lung cancer primarily to the large amount of asbestos dust he inhaled for thirteen years as a maintenance man at an asbestos factory.

Asbestos is a heat- and corrosion-resistant mineral. It is found in the natural environment and is classified as a rock. Asbestos is used widely as an insulation and also in automobile brake linings. It is the only natural mineral fiber used by man. Several kinds of mineral rocks can easily be separated into these long, white fibers. Many shingles used in home construction are made of asbestos.

Lung ailments directly associated with exposure to asbestos have, thus far, been limited to those who work with the material. Some scientists in 1969, however, singled out asbestos particles as a possibly dangerous ingredient in urban air pollution. Asbestos dust acts as a "blotter" when it penetrates into the lungs. It absorbs and holds whatever harmful substances exist in cigarette smoke or, for that matter, in the air you breathe.

Asbestos dust takes many routes into the atmosphere. Particles get into the air through the disintegration of asbestos products. During construction activity, asbestos is often sprayed on girders or beams. A typical sprayer used throughout the 1960s unleashed an asbestos-particle snowstorm each time it was used outdoors on a construction job.

Research findings have strengthened the suspicion that asbestos dust can be dangerous to city dwellers. Autopsies performed at hospitals in New York, Montreal, and Cape Town, South Africa, revealed that there were asbestos dust particles in the lungs of between 25 and 50 percent of persons who died of varied causes.

The problem is not a difficult one to solve. The first major step has been accomplished. We are aware of the possible widespread, harmful effects. There is really no technical difficulty in devising mechanical devices that can control the amount of dust generated by equipment that processes and applies asbestos. We simply must determine that we want the job done and then see to it that it is done. The lesson to be learned, however, is that we must be constantly alert to the possibility that many so-called harmless substances can become dangerous pollutants once they are unleashed in the atmosphere.

A combination of circumstances in the atmosphere combine to develop a condition fraught with disaster: a high concentration of pollutants and a stagnant air mass lying over an area for an extended period. At times, the situation is further complicated by an inversion. An air inversion exists when a colder air mass lies under a warmer air mass. This arrangement has the heavier air at ground level, and it prevents normal convection currents or the process of upward ventilation from occurring. Under such conditions, the pollutants pouring into the air simply accumulate, and concentrations build.

The word "smog" was first used in 1905. Originally, it was used to describe a combination of smoke and fog. In the popular sense today, it is used to describe any kind of objectionable pollution. We should recognize, however, that pollution does not always produce smog. And fog is not necessarily present when smog appears. There are, in fact, two types of pollution that deserve the name *smog:*

• London-type smog. This type occurs on foggy days when the temperature drops below 50° F. Great amounts of smoke, fly ash, and sulphur compounds that have been released by burning fuels such as soft coal are usually in the air. Visibility is greatly reduced by this smog, and it causes widespread bronchial irritation.

• Los Angeles-type smog. This type occurs in sunny, urban centers with great numbers of automobiles pouring out carbon monoxide and other harmful contaminants. The pollutants are usually held in place by a stationary air mass. The sunlight works on the pollutants and brings about chemical changes in the ozone, oxides of nitrogen, and the hydrocarbons. These changes, influenced by sunlight, make the pollutants more irritating than they normally would be. The Los Angeles-type

Cement dust from the Whitehall cement plant forms a haze covering parts of Lehigh Valley, Pennsylvania. Photo taken October 20, 1965.

smog is also called photochemical smog. It causes reduced visibility, eye irritation, cracking of rubber, and damage to plants.

Normally, the earth is heated by the sun; and it passes some heat to the air lying close to it. The heated air rises as a convection current. In the process of rising, its temperature drops several degrees for each thousand feet of ascent. This movement provides a type of ventilation and serves to carry pollutants into the upper atmosphere. This type of upward dispersal tends to dilute, or reduce, the concentration of pollutants. The rising bubble or stream of warm air is replaced at ground level by cooler air moving down from aloft. This new supply of air is, in turn, warmed, and rises carrying pollutants with it.

The upward ventilation system is blocked and the situation is complicated when a temperature inversion occurs, i.e, warm air above sitting on cold air at ground level. Any upward circulation of the ground-level air is blocked. The thick, warm layer lying above acts as a lid. At times, the colder air mass (cold and warm used here are relative terms) hugging the ground is stagnant, too; and there is little or no horizontal wind speed in it. Such air masses usually have high pressures and are called stagnating anticyclones. They usually linger over an area for a protracted period of four or more days. Thus a stagnating anticyclone plus a temperature inversion mean that the pollutants cannot be dispersed horizontally either.

The west coasts of continents throughout the world seem to have semipermanent inversions. The southwestern coast of the United States and the west coasts of South America, the Iberian Peninsula, and Africa all have a typical vertical lid on the upward movement of ground air. This condition is created by the downward movement of air that results from the high-pressure cells over the oceans in each area.

Another fact to remember is that the temperature profile for any area of the earth changes drastically each night when compared with the daytime conditions. At sunset, the radiation falling on the earth is suddenly cut off. From this point on, throughout the night there is rapid radiational cooling of the ground. The layer of air close to the earth also cools off. This creates an inversion of the daytime temperature profile. At night, there is usually an increase in temperature with height. Thus vertical motions in the night atmosphere are damped, or shut down. This usually prevents upward ventilation of pollutants at night. The longer hours of winter darkness favor the formation of inversions. In the polar regions, the long nighttime conditions encourage inversions that persist for weeks. The temperature differences in these polar inversions can be 36° F.

Chicago is often shrouded in smog.

Another condition that plays a big role in pollution is the natural topography of the area. The semicircular ring of hills and mountains around the Los Angeles area slows the flow of air into and out of the basin. Thus pollutants pile up and are held in the area itself. The Great Basin of Utah and Nevada functions in the same way, but on a much larger scale. This huge bowl, covering two states, can hold a stagnating air mass solidly in place. The narrow valleys of western Pennsylvania also act to slow the flow of air and cause the air movements to follow the contours of the valley. Thus pollutants are channeled so they repeatedly follow the same path and sweep over the same locale.

What does all this mean? Obviously, that meteorology and topography can set the stage for air pollution disasters. The apparent solution is to prevent all the pollutants from reaching the atmosphere. This, of course, is an ideal and one we are not

The city of Chicago uses a television camera atop the Chicago Civic Center to scan its sky. A constant TV picture is relayed to the Communications Control Center, where it is viewed by the operator. When he observes smoke, the zoom lens allows him to enlarge that specific area up to ten times. Observed violations are relayed to patrol cars for immediate investigation.

likely to achieve in the next few years. But it is the direction in which we should be moving during the 1970s.

The form and the substance of the contemporary environment is determined by the public. Each individual decision by each citizen to buy certain manufactured goods, to require and select certain automobiles, to support certain legislators, to take great or little interest in the pollutants contributed by industry, commerce, and the municipality is decisive and is finally reflected in the quality of the environment. Most people act as though they can simply pull the blinds to shut out the blight and pollution. But each of us must breathe. This is one real and intimate contact with the environment. And the filthy conditions created around us finally seep into our own bodies with each breath we must take to sustain life.

The long-term effects of this sewer in the sky result mostly in diseases of the bronchial tree that makes up each lung. Emphysema is one of these diseases attributable to air pollution in which progressive breakdown of air sacs in the lungs occurs. It is usually caused by chronic infection or constant irritation of the bronchial tubes. Gradually, this disease interferes with the ability of the lungs to transfer oxygen and to remove carbon dioxide from the bloodstream.

In 1969, six times as many deaths resulted from emphysema as occurred in 1950. During the decade of the 1950s, the death rate increased sixfold. Emphysema continued to claim more lives during the decade of the 1960s, with twice as many people dying in cities from this cause as died in rural areas. All the studies have indicated that the emphysema patient improves when he is protected from air pollution by simply filtering the air.

Bronchial asthma is another condition aggravated by air pollution. Bronchitis, pneumonia, and lung cancer are other diseases that are affected by the level of atmospheric pollution. Certainly many factors are involved in each of these diseases, but there seems to be little doubt that one factor that can aggravate and increase the mortality rate in each case is air pollution.

The major gaseous pollutants can be divided into two types: acid gases and photochemical gases. Sulphur dioxide, hydrogen fluoride, and carbon monoxide are considered acid gases. Ozone and peroxyacetyl nitrate (PAN) are counted as photochemical

Compare these scenes of New York City. They were taken on different days at essentially the same location on the New Jersey side of the Hudson River. One of the photos is a definite smoggy view of New York.

gases. Some scientists suggest that the photochemical gases usually cause damage over much wider areas than the acid gases. This conclusion is supported by research on vegetation.

Some factors make certain people much more sensitive than others to carbon monoxide poisoning: heart disease, anemia, asthma, lung impairment, poor circulation, high temperature, high altitude, and high humidity. That's quite a list, isn't it? When a sensitive person is exposed to as little as 30 ppm of carbon dioxide for eight consecutive hours, there may be a serious risk to his health. A concentration of 100 ppm for one hour can also be quite harmful.

Ozone severely irritates the mucous membranes of man. At levels normally found in many cities during the 1960s, a ten-minute exposure was sufficient to cause irritation. Coughing, choking, and severe fatigue have also been attributed to this pollutant. In research studies, the lives of guinea pigs were significantly shortened and the death rate increased by continuous low-level exposure to ozone. Green plants are particularly sensitive to ozone. The injuries produced are usually restricted to the old leaves and show up as tip burn, spots, streaks, flecks, and stipple.

PAN produces a disorder in the youngest, fully expanded leaves of green plants called *silver leaf*. This pollutant has been identified as a cause of eye irritation in man, and it is suspected in a number of lung infections.

Sulphur dioxide has a long, well-documented history of harmful effects. The presence of moisture in the lungs aggravates the effect of the oxides of sulphur on the tissue. The presence of moisture on plant leaves also intensifies the damage done by this pollutant. The symptom of injury is the development of spots bleached a light tan color on the plant leaves. Occasionally, the margins of the leaves are also killed.

Beryllium, used as a fuel for rocket engines and in the production of metallic alloys has produced cancerous tumors in monkeys. Fluorides discharged into the atmosphere during the production of aluminum, steel, and phosphate fertilizers has caused severe damage to cattle and to vegetation. Lead added to gasolines finally works its way into the atmosphere. It is taken into the human body in food and in water, as well as in the air that we breathe. Lead is a cumulative poison. It works on the brain as well as other parts of the central nervous system.

Air pollution is a complex problem. There should be little doubt in anyone's mind, however, that it deserves a high priority on the list of problems crying for solution in the 1970s.

Chapter 6

OUR DEPENDENCE ON FRESH WATER

Next to the air we breathe, water is our most important resource: without it we can live for only a very short time. Almost 70 percent of the human body consists of water. Each of man's almost one trillion body cells must receive an abundant supply to carry on vital functions, including using oxygen, taking in food, and getting rid of waste.

Other animals and plants are as dependent on water as man. Mice, elephants, and an ear of corn each contain about the same percentage of water as your bodies do. Potatoes and earthworms run as high as 80 percent, while a ripe, juicy tomato is 95 percent water.

For the most part, Americans have thought of water as a common, ordinary substance. By world standards, we always regarded our nation as rich in water. But at the turn of the twentieth century, some concern began to develop about the quality of our supply. As one example, we can cite conditions along the Missouri River. During the first decade of this century, there were about one million people living along this river. The Missouri supplied the drinking water for the majority of these people. Even so, raw sewage was dumped directly into the river. There just weren't any sewage treatment plants. The few purification systems that did exist at the time were not very adequate. And throughout those years, waterborne epidemics were quite common. These epidemics alerted some people to the trouble that lay ahead.

At midcentury, over two million people were drinking water from the Missouri River. Raw sewage, however, was still pouring into the water. And as late as 1954, there were no sewage treatment plants along this river. But by this time the cities did have extensive water treatment plants. These treatment facilities were

This child in San Jorge, Guatemala knows the value of water. By world standards, we in the United States are fortunate. But our good fortune has not been appreciated. We have squandered our most precious resource.

the only sentinels standing between the people and catastrophic epidemics.

Gradually, an attitude of crisis began to grow. It built slowly during the last half of the 1950s. Events of the 1960s focused attention on the dangerously low water levels of the Great Lakes The blight and pollution of these lakes, along with the imminent death of Lake Erie, shocked the national pride. Almost as if eyes were opening for the first time, the polluted condition of our rivers and lakes were seen and recorded in newspapers and magazines across the country. An increased demand on the part of the people to set new levels of cleanliness for our waters was heard. And during 1965, the shock of the worst floods in twenty-five years striking the Midwest followed by the worst drought in over a hundred years in the Northeast convinced everyone of the need for action without further delay to save our water resources.

But there seems to be a history of astonishing lethargy concerning environmental health problems. The report of the Task Force on Environmental Health in June 1967 to the Secretary of Health, Education, and Welfare indicates that a crisis situation was continuing at the end of the 1960s:

"Fifty million Americans drink water that does not meet Public Health Service drinking water standards. Another forty-five million Americans drink water that has not been tested by the Public Health Service. Alarming as this situation sounds, it could easily be either more or less ominous, since the Task Force is not satisfied that the present Public Health Service standards for drinking water adequately reflect the health needs of the people.

"Therefore, the Task Force recommends that the Department undertake an effort by 1970 to test all existing and proposed public drinking water supply systems and produce meaningful public drinking water standards which, through an enforcement program, will ensure health-approved drinking water for 100 percent of the nation's public systems."

Terrible! There is no other way to describe the situation, especially when you realize that six thousand of the nineteen thousand public drinking water systems of the United States at the end of the 1960s were not able to meet federal standards for the quality of drinking water. And remember, the adequacy of the standards was questioned by the 1967 Task Force. The situation is critical.

Chemically pure water is nothing but a compound of two atoms of hydrogen and one of oxygen, written as H_2O. It can exist as a liquid, solid, or gas. Water is, in fact, the only chemical that exists naturally in the narrow temperature ranges of the earth in these three states. It has the further distinction of being one of the few natural liquids on earth.

Water has some unusual physical and chemical characteristics. These properties make water unique in its ability to protect and support life:

• *Maximum density point.* Most matter contracts as it is cooled and expands when it is heated. Water, however, has its maximum density at 39.2° F. It expands when heated or cooled from this point. Thus, as chemically pure water is cooled from 39° F to 32° F, it expands until it becomes ice, i.e., solid water. This is most important to life in a pond, lake, or river. As water is cooled below 39° F, it rises to the top of the water surface. A lake, for example, freezes at the top. Life can still function below the frozen surface.

• *Heat capacity.* Water has a tremendous "heat capacity." It can absorb a great amount of heat without a large increase in temperature. Thus large amounts of radiation from the sun can be absorbed by lake water without significantly affecting the environmental temperature of plant and animal life. This property of water provides a tempering effect on climate. The water in large lakes, rivers, bays, and oceans literally "sops up" heat.

• *Strong internal bonds.* A molecule of chemically pure water has strong internal bonds that bind the oxygen and hydrogen together. Because of the strength of these bonds, water resists separation into its atoms. For that reason, pure water is a very poor conductor of electricity. And because of its strong internal bonds, it maintains its characteristic properties and identity under all but the most drastic conditions.

• *A good solvent.* The molecular structure of water allows it to dissolve and hold other chemicals in solution. When pure water contains dissolved chemicals, it is acting as a solvent. This property that keeps dissolved substances in solution is water's most remarkable property. In a human, water acts as a solvent, carrying many different chemicals in solution throughout the body. Water is also the usual solvent in other animals, and in plants as well.

Water, in nature, is never really chemically pure. Pure water is H_2O, nothing else. Water, as it rises from the ocean as vapor, is H_2O; however, as it condenses and falls as rain, it quickly gathers dust, gases, smoke, and microscopic, living organisms. The solvent action of water even allows it to pick up minerals being carried by the winds. Thus, rainwater, after a short fall through the atmosphere, contains a number of dissolved and suspended materials.

Rain water from the roof of a building in Becquia, an island in the Caribbean, is collected in the cistern and used for drinking water.

Rainwater can be considered fresh. But it is not chemically pure. Whether the fresh rainwater can be used for drinking purposes is another problem. If a "Yes" or a 'No" answer is desired, then we must look into the nature of the dissolved materials in the fresh water. The question to be asked is: "What effect will these dissolved and suspended materials have on a human who drinks the water?" The answer will determine if the quality of the water is adequate for the purpose intended, that is, drinking.

At the end of the 1960s, there was virtually no information on the health implications of minute amounts or traces of materials found in drinking water. There is some suspicion that some of these substances do produce disease after a long period of time. Selenium, for example, is a rare element sometimes found in minute quantities in drinking water. A family living near Ignacio, Colorado, in 1962 suffered hair loss, weakened nails, and listlessness from drinking well water containing selenium. Even the family dog lost its hair. The well was drilled in the Wasatch geological formation and was used for household purposes for almost three months before the symptoms began to show.

Anything other than H_2O found in water is classified as an impurity. Generally, these impurities may be grouped into four categories:
• living organisms
• dissolved gases
• dissolved solids
• suspended substances

As water from rain, snow, sleet, and hail moves across the land, it often becomes turbid, or cloudy. This condition results from the silt, sand, mud, and clay carried in suspension. The kinds of solid particles that the water picks up depend on the kind of land it moves over as it makes its way to brooks, streams, rivers, and finally back to the ocean. Days, weeks, months, or in the case of glacial ice, even years may pass before the precipitation works its way back to the sea.

The longer the water stays in contact with the environment, the more opportunity it has to pick up impurities. Water can, in fact, take on color and many organic impurities from the domestic and industrial wastes poured into our rivers. Color and organic impurities can also be picked up naturally as water flows through a swampy area. Decaying plants and animals often give water an objectionable taste and odor.

Some of the water falling to earth seeps into the ground. The earth acts as a filter, removing micro-organisms and turbidity. When ground water is retrieved for use by means of a well, it is usually found to be clearer than it was as surface water. But the ground water usually contains greater concentrations of dissolved minerals than the surface water. Calcium and magnesium from the earth's crust are the most abundant of the dissolved minerals. Water containing these minerals is said to be "hard." Extremely hard water may contain more than 190 ppm of these minerals. The hardness of surface water varies. Lake Michigan, to cite one example, has a hardness of 125 ppm, but you can find all kinds of variations.

Iron and manganese are among some of the minerals that frequently are found in water. These impurities give water a metallic taste. As little as 0.3 ppm of iron can cause trouble. Water that contains iron may appear colorless as it is first drawn from the faucet. The invisible dissolved iron, however, will eventually combine with oxygen from the air to form a reddish-brown precipitate, especially after heating in a tea kettle.

An offensive gaseous impurity found in some water supplies is hydrogen sulphide. There is no mistaking it; the "rotten egg" odor can be detected with concentrations as low as 1 ppm.

Carbonic acid, mineral acids, and industrial acids often work their way into supplies to make corrosive water. The problem usually produces water that is rusty. The acids attack the pipes through which the water moves. When such a condition exists, you will be aware of it because of the reddish stains from iron pipes and of the blue-green stains from copper pipes.

Flouride is found in both surface water and ground water. It occurs in greater concentrations in ground water, however. When there is more than 1.5 ppm in drinking water, it can cause brown stains or mottling on tooth enamel. At concentrations of 1 ppm, fluoride has a definite beneficial effect in that it can substantially reduce tooth decay. Excessive fluoride should be removed from water.

Nitrates and phosphates get into water through fertilizers, leguminous plants, plant debris, and bacterial decomposition. Human and animal wastes are another source by which these minerals enter water supplies. Most of our present waste disposal treatment systems also add nitrate and phosphate to water. A nitrate concentration in water of 45 ppm is definitely unsafe. As little as 8 ppm in an infant's drinking water can cause death. Nitrates decrease the oxygen-carrying capacity of the blood. The symptom that indicates a child is in real trouble is a blueness of the skin called *cyanosis.* Many physicians recommend that water containing more than 3 ppm not be given to an infant or used in the preparation of his formula. By the end of the 1960s, many water supplies in the United States had reached levels of 3 ppm.

The oceans are not the only areas where salty and highly mineralized water is found. There are many inland waters that are classified as brackish or saline. The dissolved solids in sea water run from 33,000 to 36,000 ppm. Brackish and saline water are less salty than sea water, but they do contain large amounts of dissolved solids. Water is defined as brackish when it contains 1000 to 3000 ppm and as saline when its concentration of minerals is in the range from 3000 to 10,000 ppm. During the 1960s, over one thousand municipal water supplies were drawn from brackish water, while thirty-one municipalities drew supplies from water that was definitely saline.

There are slightly more than eighteen thousand community sewer systems in the United States. Only about fourteen thousand of these operate sewage treatment plants. In addition, there are more than thirty thousand water-using industries that have separate waste outlets. Thus approximately fifty thousand major locations exist throughout the country that accumulate large concentrations of waste, and millions of homes, small industrial operations, and farms are not included in this count. Each location—large or small—has its own problem of waste management.

Waste management has not been very satisfactory over the years. Detergents, radioactive material, organic contaminants, and other wastes have found their way into the water supplies of this nation and the world. The vast quantities of these wastes that have been poured into our streams, rivers, and lakes have

Note the distinct line of demarcation between the polluted waters of a tributary and the waters of Lake Ontario, outside Rochester Harbor.

"overwhelmed" the natural systems of these waters so that their ability to cleanse themselves has been lessened and, in some cases, completely destroyed.

During the summer of 1968, water weeds (principally water milfoil) choked New Jersey waterways. The rapid growth of unwanted grasses and algae was caused by the flow of nutrients from the land into Barnegat Bay, the Metedeconk River, and almost all of the state's inland lakes and ponds. At Lake Hopatcong, big-leaf pond weed flourished. The stringy, smelly growths clogged boat motors and closed many areas to swimmers.

Water weeds are growing in this lake. Too many lakes have become clogged by these growths in recent years.

Chemical poisoning was the prime technique used in 1968 to kill the weeds in New Jersey. These poisons are referred to as herbicides. It is an expensive method to employ, and the herbicides also disrupt certain biological cycles in the natural environment. Dredging to remove the muck from the bottom of the lake is a more intelligent approach. The nutrients that nourish the weeds are held in the muck. Remove the nutrients and you inhibit the growth of the weeds.

A still better approach, however, is to employ the checks and balances found in nature. For example, alligatorweed is a costly aquatic pest found in waterways in southern states. An insect, the flea beetle, keeps this weed under control in South America. The beetle is not known to feed on any other plant except alligatorweed and its one close relative. These insects are not natives of the United States. In the event that these insects would not produce any other harmful effects, they might be imported to control alligatorweed. Weed-destroying insects are one of the checks and balances nature uses. In the long run, they might be our best bet for the control of aquatic plant growth.

A natural purification process is a dam that limits and controls pollution. Oxygen is the key that unlocks the process and keeps it functioning. The process works in this way: Bacteria of decay in a waterway change organic wastes into inorganic substances—carbon dioxide, nitrates, phosphates. These inorganic substances nourish the plants. The plants, in turn, provide food as well as oxygen to support animals and the bacteria of decay. This is a tight little cycle of dependent events that breaks down pollutants into harmless, inoffensive forms and maintains the quality of the water and the population of plants, animals, and micro-organisms.

Runaway pollution always results when the natural purification system of a body of water is destroyed. For example, the biological balance of nature's purification system is overwhelmed when huge amounts of phosphate and nitrate enter a waterway. When these nutrients exist in overabundant concentrations, they spur the growth of algae. The algae become very dense, reach a climax, and then suddenly die. The death of large numbers of plants again overloads the water with organic debris and produces visable, unhealthy pollution.

The biological cycle of the natural purification process can assimilate only a limited amount of added organic materials and still maintain its balance. A steadily increasing organic waste load strains and breaks the balance. For example, the bacteria that change organic wastes must have oxygen. But as the waste load increases, it usually decreases the available oxygen in the water. As the oxygen content falls to zero, the bacteria die and the biological cycle breaks down, the natural purification process stops functioning, and the water develops levels of pollution from which it cannot naturally recover.

In the eighteenth and nineteenth centuries, the natural purification processes were functioning in most or all of the waterways of the United States. Prior to the twentieth century, there were limited, small amounts of pollutants in comparison to the relatively large water volume. The population growth and rapid industrialization of the country caused a tremendous increase in wastes. The volume of water available was, relatively speaking, not large enough to assimilate the waste and allow the natural purification process to function.

Nitrate and phosphates from sewage, industrial plants, and land runoff are not the only wastes that overwhelm and pollute the biological system of a lake, river, or bay. Some, or all, of the following wastes find their way into our waterways each day:
- sewage from pleasure boats and commercial ships
- inorganic and organic chemicals from detergents, pesticides, herbicides, and industrial processes
- oils as spillage from pleasure boats, commercial ships, tankers, and drilling rigs
- acids from mines and industrial processing
- disease-causing bacteria, primarily from sewage
- radioactive wastes from mining, ore processing, and commercial operations
- debris from construction and other activities
- metals from industrial processes

In the process of sewage treatment, nitrates and phosphates are produced. The most difficult problem faced by engineers is the removal of these compounds from the effluent, or discharge water. It is an almost impossible and terribly expensive task. The effluent from the most modern sewage disposal plant often contains huge concentrations of these nitrates and phosphates. And these are the compounds that overfertilize and upset the biological balance of the receiving waters so that its natural purification system is overwhelmed. In the end, the river becomes a virtual sewer anyway; fish suffocate and the water cannot be used downstream.

Restoration of the natural purification systems of our waterways is the only way of really surmounting our water pollution problems and maintaining clean water. But this restoration does not seem to be achievable unless we can withhold the huge amounts of nitrates and phosphates presently being dumped into these waters along with the treated wastes.

An experimental project undertaken at Pennsylvania State University reported, on the basis of five years of experience, that it is possible to take the effluent from a sewage treatment plant and use it to irrigate forest and crop lands. The treated water was sprayed over a special tract of farm-and-forest land. The water percolated through the soil and was filtered. The nutrients in the water, including the nitrogen and phosphorus, were deposited in the soil. The plants and soil micro-organisms utilized these nutrients to grow and develop. Over the five-year period, there was no sign of overfertilization or of poisoning of the land by these elements.

This process is not mere irrigation. It is a method of purification in which the water is filtered by the soil. In a sense, this method imitates the processes operating in nature. Clean water is returned to the earth as ground water. It is held as a water reserve and is not lost to the river and, eventually, to the ocean. And, most important, the waterways are spared the burden of all the extra nitrogen and phosphorus.

It is possible to spray treated sewage water over the land on a round-the-year basis. This procedure provides a solution to the disruption of the natural purification system of waterways. In addition, the soil is enriched, and trees and other plants grow more rapidly. Birds and other animals in the treated area also thrive. And drinkable water is stored away as an underground supply that eventually works its way into the streams and rivers. The experimental work indicated that 390 acres is sufficient to handle the treated sewage water from a town of thirty thousand people.

We can place the wastes that pollute our environment in two general categories: conventional and dispersed pollutants. Each of these categories of pollutants presents a unique problem that must be solved in order for proper handling and treatment to occur.

• *Conventional pollution.* Human waste, organic materials from food processing, suspended solids, and toxic residues from industrial processing are included in this group. For the most part, these wastes can be traced to particular sources and locations. We can collect these wastes and take them into treatment facilities where they can be processed, using the best-known technology. Then we can make decisions as to what to do with the effluents and solid materials that result from the treatment process.

To handle conventional pollution, we must expand our waste treatment facility construction programs. Various costs have been projected. Conservative estimates are that, if we had begun the expansion program on a national scale in the 1960s, we would have needed to spend twenty billion dollars and we could have protected three-fourths of our people by the mid-1970s. We did not start a national program in the 1960s and, thus, an increased amount of money will need to be spent because of the delay. Again, a conservative estimate is that one hundred billion dollars spent between now and the year 2000 could give us an *adequate* program of public and private sanitary and industrial waste treatment. That is a lot of money. But it is the price we must pay for centuries of neglect. We have no choice but to make the commitment. If the American people make the decision, we have the resources to get the job done. If we don't make the commitment, we can assume that we are writing and starring in a tragedy of our own making.

In the handling of conventional pollution—especially from our homes and small industrial plants—there is a little-recognized problem: overworked drainage systems. A community may have a sewage treatment plant, *but* it may also have only one sewer system that handles wastes from homes and industrial plants as well as the rainwater from the city streets. When a storm strikes, the drains are quickly filled to capacity. In such emergencies, the treatment plants pass the unprocessed overflow, sewage and all, directly into the rivers.

In the United States we have the problem of overworked sewer systems. But in too many places in the world there are open sewers, such as this one found on St. Vincent, an island in the Caribbean.

A summer storm in Chicago during 1968 filled its combined storm and sewer system to overflow. The Chicago treatment plant had to pass a twelve-mile-long slug of waste into Lake Michigan. Chicago plans to dig great caverns beneath the city to hold the overflow that occurs during storms. This stored sewage would then be drawn through the treatment plant at a later time.

One of two one-hundred-thousand-gallon rubberized Pillow tanks, designed to hold sewage overflow caused by heavy rains, is prepared for submerging in the Anacostia River, Washington, D.C.

The Minneapolis-St. Paul Sanitary District has the same problem of a single drainage system that becomes overwhelmed during storms and at other periods. A computer is being used around the clock to monitor the quality of the sewer water. The computer directs the most polluted flow to the treatment plant, while the less polluted flow is allowed to move directly into the river. A sum of 1.75 million dollars was spent on the installation of the computer in 1968. It may help, but polluted sewage will still be passed raw into the river.

Collapsible one-hundred-thousand-gallon tanks of rubber-impregnated nylon were anchored at the bottom of the Anacostia River in Washington, D.C., in 1968. These tanks will serve the same purpose as the Chicago underground caverns, i.e., when the drains are filled by rain and sewage the overflow will be diverted by the pumphouse into the tanks for storage until the sewage can be processed.

These three techniques (in Chicago, Minneapolis-St. Paul, and Washington, D.C.) are really only stopgap procedures. The only effective solution is to build two separate drainage systems: one for sewage, the other for water runoff. The estimated national pricetag, at this point, is thirty billion dollars. Should it be done? What value do you put on the health of the natural environment in which man must live?

• *Dispersed Pollutants.* This whole category of wastes is essentially uncollectable. In this category, for example, fall the fertilizers, herbicides, fungicides, insecticides, and radioactive wastes. Each of these materials is let loose on the environment by man's activity. They are dispersed and move into the stream of activity in the natural environment. They defy ordinary treatment because they cannot be collected, concentrated, and brought to a conventional treatment plant.

These wastes, however, do build up in water supplies. Their presence in water makes it, at times, undesirable, even dangerous for a multitude of human and industrial uses. We are only beginning to learn about the dangers of long-term, low-level exposure to some of these wastes. But of this we can be certain: No waste can be written off as harmless!

There is an insufficient amount of research concerning how these dispersed, chemically complex wastes can be treated. A promising report, however, indicates that two species of algae can be used to combat pesticides. *Chlorella vulgaris* and *Chlamydomonas reinhardtii* are able to metabolize the pesticide lindane. It may be possible to place these algae in a lindane-contaminated water supply to clean it up. Another possibility is to place these algae in drainage ditches around a field treated with lindane. Thus the spread of the pesticide beyond the area might be prevented.

DDT is another of the insecticides that has entered our waterways and has been concentrated in the bodies of marine animals. It was found recently that primitive soil insects of the class Collembola are able to metabolize DDT (dichlorodiphenyltrichloroethane) and break it down to DDE (dichlorodiphenyldichloroethylene). DDE is relatively nontoxic to beneficial soil organisms and warm-blooded animals. These primitive soil insects might be used as a DDT cleanup squad.

The chemical, petroleum, pulp and paper, steel, automobile, textile, leather, soap, and detergent producers are the largest industrial users of water. They are also potentially the largest contaminators of the nation's water supplies. It should be stressed that the larger companies have huge investments in waste treatment facilities. And even though many of them still have problems with their discharge water, there is every indication that a new breed of industrialist is acting responsibly. This does not mean, however, that the public should be less adamant in demanding that the pace of industrial pollution control be quickened.

Paper mills, especially, must be required drastically to limit the discharge of inert pulp wastes. These materials pollute and destroy the balance in streams so that no life can survive. The water from such streams is unfit for human as well as industrial use. Cement plants are also great offenders. Large-scale discharges of limestone tailings spell disaster for the biological cycle.

Some of the larger steel producers have done an excellent job of pollution control. The coal industry, too, should be congratulated for the progress made in the control of acid waters from mines and the reclamation work done on abandoned strip piles. For every good example that can be cited, however, there are still too many offenders. And one offender offsets the good work of hundreds of responsible people. One is too many to tolerate!

The addition of heat to our waterways as a result of various commercial operations poses one of the most difficult problems in water pollution control. Waste heat discharge into our streams and rivers has increased rapidly since the 1940s. Heated water discharged from electric power plants is one of the main sources of this type of pollution. Let it be clear. We need electric power today, and our nation's requirements for this kind of power are growing. Thus the dimensions of the problem enlarge with each passing year. In fact, the electric power generating capacity has been doubling every decade since the mid-1940s. And the prospect is that the doubling of our power needs and production will occur at five-year intervals in the future.

In 1968, power plants in the United States discharged fifty trillion gallons of heated water into streams and rivers. By 1980, the power industry will be using more than a fifth of the nation's stream flow for cooling purposes. Today, the water is taken in from a stream, run through the power plant, and sent back to the stream 10 to 20° F warmer than it was at the start of the cooling cycle.

Thermal pollution is not smelly, but it is potentially dangerous because small changes in water temperature can have unsettling effects on the plant-animal balance. One such effect would occur when an increase in water temperature causes a fish hatch to occur so early in the spring that the fishes' natural food is not available. Aquatic plants, a basic part of the food chain, depend on day length as well as temperature and, thus, will lag behind an early fish hatch caused by temperature alone. The plant-animal balance is also unsettled by temperature because the sensitivity of plants to toxic materials present in water is increased as temperatures increase. The net effect of a temperature rise, then, may be a decrease in availability of plant material.

The really crucial effect of thermal pollution, however, relates to the oxygen content of the waterways. As water temperatures rise, the water cannot hold as much oxygen in solution. So rising stream temperatures mean less oxygen in the water. On the other hand, as temperatures rise, aquatic vertebrates, fish, for example, need more oxygen. In fact, fish require as much oxygen for every 18° F increase in temperature. Thus the same conditions that decrease the amount of oxygen available in the water also produce an increased need for oxygen in certain of the animals living in the water.

The problem of thermal pollution is not a terribly difficult one to solve. The simplest solution available is to use cooling towers to dissipate the heat. The waste heat, however, can even be put to constructive use rather than be discharged into the atmosphere from the tower. For example, the heat can be used for industrial process heating, desalting water, and the heating of buildings. Thus to save our streams from thermal pollution we simply need to decide to build an effective installation that dissipates the heat, or uses it: Let me state again that we should provide good profit incentives for those producers of electric power who handle their problems effectively.

Some heated water is sent back to sea by way of the blowdown to the harbor.

The southernmost city in the continental United States, Key West, is on a coral island more than one hundred miles southwest of the mainland. An overseas highway runs from the mainland to the city along bridges and causeways connecting a whole series of small coral islands.

In 1941, the people of Key West began satisfying their thirst for fresh water using a 130-mile-long pipeline that was built from the Florida mainland. Prior to that year, fresh water was obtained by barge or from rainfall. By the early 1960s, six million gallons of fresh water were being drawn from the 130-mile soda straw. The daily supply was not adequate to meet the growing needs of fifty thousand people in the Key West area.

Ground breaking for a desalination plant to convert salt water from the Atlantic Ocean to fresh water took place on July 12, 1966. The plant was in full operation in 1967. At that time, it was the largest single-unit desalting plant in the world. It has a capacity of 2.62 million gallons per day. The cost of the desalted water in 1968 was eighty-five cents per thousand gallons.

The operation is simple. Sea water is drawn from sea water wells. The water from these wells is filtered through the limestone strata beneath the site to make sure it is free of seaweed, algae, and marine life. This natural filtering eliminates all the costly problems associated with the usual sea water intake systems. The sea water is heated and introduced into a chamber in which the pressure is reduced. When the heated sea water enters the low-pressure chamber, some of it immediately "flashes" into vapor. It is then passed to a moisture separator and condensed to form the distilled product: fresh water. This flash process is repeated over and over again. Heat from the condensing vapors is transferred to cold sea water in a condenser system. Then a portion of this heated sea water is discharged back into the sea.

The desalination operation at Key West literally makes the Atlantic Ocean—all 31,030,000 square miles of it—a reservoir to be tapped and used. And this fresh water opens up a completely new growth for the area that will only begin to be realized in the 1970s. There are a lot of communities in this world that can benefit from desalination. The Key West operation uses oil as its fuel. Atomic energy will more than likely be the important fuel for future desalination plants.

The future of man is intimately related to the fresh water available to him. Fresh water comes to man from the sea through the natural water cycle. Man, through desalination, can also dip directly into the sea to get his fresh water. If, however, we are to benefit fully from nature's gift of fresh water that falls on our land, we must then be concerned with the health of the environment into which the fresh water falls. Man must exert a measure of positive control over his environment—but it must be a control that improves rather than a control that debilitates and destroys.

Chapter 7

THE POLLUTION OF LAND
AND SOIL

Air and water are the factors in environmental health that seem to be stressed the most. But there is another equally important aspect of the environment that needs thoughtful attention: the land. It is the land, after all, that inherits most of the solid waste from urban, commercial, industrial, and agricultural activities. And when water and air pollution control are *practiced,* it is the land that receives the unwanted solid and liquid wastes that are withheld from these other parts of the environment.

The population growth has sent homes and industrial plants sprawling over the countryside. Spreading urbanization has not only multiplied the problems of air and water pollution, but it has raised serious questions of land use, solid waste disposal, and the preservation of the landscape and green areas.

Each day, people in New York City discard more than sixteen thousand tons of garbage and refuse. During the course of the year, this amounts to almost six million tons. New York is not unique. In most areas of the nation, the refuse disposal problem has reached critical proportions.

The problem has been with us and has been growing rapidly during the last half century. In 1920, fifty million tons of garbage were disposed of, primarily by dumping. There was not a significant increase during the next decade, and there was no pressure to do away with the open city dump. In fact, children, dogs, cats, and rats alike frolicked in the city dumps of the 1930s and found many things to interest them.

By 1940, the refuse pile of the nation was building noticeably. Some seventy-five million tons accumulated during that year, and by 1950 the annual tonnage was one hundred million. In the next fifteen years there was little doubt that the junk pile was getting out of hand. In 1965, well over 150 million tons were collected. And, within the next few years, an additional fifty million tons were added to the yearly total. By 1980, the refuse collection will exceed 250 million tons; and we will be well on our way to three hundred million tons by 1990.

At Bethlehem Steel's Mine No. 44 near Idamay, West Virginia, there is lush, ankle-high cover of bluegrass, fescue, lespedeza, and rye grass growing on a former coal tailings basin. There, as in other Bethlehem mine locations, the grass was planted by the relatively new technique of hydroseeding. Hydroseeding consists of making a soupy mixture of water, fertilizer, grass seed, and paper pulp mulch, then spraying it over the area. The pulp mulch serves to hold the seed in place and also to retain moisture to accelerate the germination of the grass seed.

In the Middle Ages, people dumped garbage out of windows. For most of the twentieth century, we have done very little better. The skies over the bustling dumps of the 1930s and 1940s were daily filled with black clouds from the open fires. And in too many towns like Bayonne and Jersey City, New Jersey, too many people could look out their windows and see the daily line of dump trucks waiting to unload. Gradually, during the 1950s, landfill and other procedures were adopted; but the open dump was not given up completely. It is not difficult to locate these lingering, festering sores on the land as you ride through the countryside.

Another trend in our refuse pile is its changing character. The refuse of thirty years ago was principally garbage and ashes. Today the rubbish pile can consist of everything from dead animals, demolition refuse, old appliances, industrial waste, construction refuse, and nonreturnable containers and bottles to hazardous and special wastes from hospitals or nuclear power plants.

Burning, or incineration, is the most popular solid waste disposal technique today. Supposedly, it is a clean way of disposing of the problem. In fact, however, most incinerators transform most of the solids to smoke, airborne dirt, and poisons. This simply changes the nature of the problem from one of land pollution to one of air pollution. The only time burning refuse should be acceptable is when the incinerator is equipped with effective pollution-control equipment.

The residue remaining after burning commonly totals 5 to 20 percent of the refuse volume at most incinerators. The residue can be used as a subbase material for new roads. Most cities, however, dispose of the residue in landfills. Some incinerator plant operations—especially in Europe—harness and sell the waste heat. Atlanta, Georgia, sells heat to commercial buildings. The heat generated by the incinerator plant in Miami, Florida, is used to heat a hospital and to pump water. At Oceanside, New York, the heat from the incinerator is used to supply steam to operate a desalting plant there.

Composting is an alternative to incineration of refuse. It is the process that salvages the "gold in your garbage." Composting (as applied to waste disposal) is the biological decomposition of the organic component of refuse. Experimental composting plants have been very successful.

We are standing on a hill in Jersey City. The houses and factories above are in Hoboken, New Jersey. In the upper right-hand corner of the photograph is the Empire State Building in New York City. Remember, the Hudson River runs between Hoboken and New York. From our vantage point, we see a jumble of factories, tenements, apartment houses, and skyscrapers. People seem to be piled on people!

There is a lot of scrap to salvage.

When garbage arrives at a composting plant, it is placed in a receiving pit. In the pit, bulky items are removed for salvage or reduced in size. Magnets and pickers remove other salvageable items as the refuse moves on a conveyor belt to a pulverizer and finally to a grinder. The finely pulverized material is sent to a digester, where it undergoes six days of processing. Finally, when it comes out, it is somewhat comparable to peat moss or leaf mold.

Experimental composting plants were operating at Phoenix, Elmira, Houston, and the Virgin Islands in the mid-1960s. Composting has not really caught on in the United States. Many experimental plants are started and then are closed because of the expense involved. Composting, however, is relatively popular in Italy, Austria, the Netherlands, and Israel. The market for the soil conditioner, or compost, is the key to the success of this type of operation. In Israel, for example, they are striving to grow crops in sandy soil. In fact, the plants in Haifa and Tel Aviv can't meet the demands for the compost.

In the past, most agricultural wastes were simply returned to the land to help enrich its yield. But today the farm is run like an industrial operation. Beef cattle and poultry spend much of their lives in the confines of a feedlot or poultry house. The farmers prefer the cheap, concentrated, easy-to-apply commercial fertilizers. And so the manure accumulates. A lot of it, too! One cow can produce as much as twenty-five pounds of manure for every pound of weight gained. A cow producing one pound of milk will also produce three pounds of manure in the process.

It has been estimated that the manure produced by the nation's livestock each year would cover the state of Rhode Island to a depth of several inches. The manure of the United States is not spread across Rhode Island; but it is being allowed, in some cases, to accumulate in growing piles on farms at the far reaches of the city. The fly populations that develop and thrive around these manure piles are unbelievable. Concentrations of manure stockpiles also lead to severe drainage problems.

Today, armies of men and fleets of trucks are used to haul garbage from individual households to a landfill area, incinerator, or compost plant. Collection and transportation is the major cost in solid-waste disposal. New York City, for example, had a sanitation department of fourteen thousand men in 1968. Some eighteen hundred garbage trucks roll along that city's streets each day.

In Sweden and Great Britain, a rather reasonable scheme for transporting wastes has been developed. Some of their large, scattered apartment complexes have been fitted with pneumatic tubes that transport household refuse to central incinerators as much as a mile and a half away.

A research study carried on at the University of Pennsylvania during 1967 showed that it is possible to collect and pump wastes in a thin, watery mixture (slurry) that resembles mud. Ordinary household wastes—food, scraps, bones, metal containers, and bottles—can be pulverized in powerful household grinders. When this pulverized refuse is mixed with small amounts of water, it becomes slurry and it can be pumped through pipes as small as two inches in diameter.

Once the slurry is in the pipes, it can be pumped out of town more cheaply than it can be trucked out. It is possible to place these small solid-waste lines inside existing sewer lines. The solid wastes in slurry form can be piped to far-off places. Landfill, for example, is genuinely needed in the abandoned strip mines of Pennsylvania. Solid-waste lines could be used to transport slurry from New York to Pennsylvania.

There are other possibilities for using the slurry of solid wastes. For example, metals, glass, and certain plastics can be recovered from it. Then the organic material of the slurry can be mixed with the semisolid sludge residues of sewage treatment plants. The manure from domestic animals can be placed into this mix, and a rich compost can be formed. Think of the land, here and abroad, that might be improved by such a compost.

On January 21, 1968, a U. S. Air Force B-52 crashed. A tragedy under any circumstance! But the crash required a special cleanup procedure because four hydrogen bombs were being carried aboard the airplane.

The four bombs broke open as a result of the crash. The highly toxic plutonium, the fissionable material of the bomb, was spread across the landscape of North Star Bay in Greenland. Ice and hard-packed snow over an area of five hundred by two thousand feet was contaminated by the radioactive plutonium.

Caution and quick action are needed when such contamination

is let loose. Fortunately, the tragedy occurred during the winter. The ice and snow were frozen and did not melt to spread the radioactive material into the Atlantic. But cleanup time was at a premium because spring and summer thaws were not far off. And if any of the contaminant got into the water, difficulties would develop. Eskimos living in the area depend on seal, walrus, and mussels for their food. Contaminants in the water would certainly affect the mussel beds as well as the local seal and walrus herds.

Bulldozers were used to clear the crash area well before the summer thaw. The ice and snow were scraped up and pushed into steel containers. The volume of snow and ice removed was enormous. The tanks used held up to eighteen thousand gallons each. Each container was sealed so that no contaminated moisture could escape. Then the tanks were stored to await the summer thaw, when North Star Bay can be reached by sea. The tanks containing the radioactive snow and ice were shipped to the Atomic Energy Commission's Savannah River plant in South Carolina for an atomic-age burial.

The accident at North Star Bay is frightening because we can sense the danger to which life is exposed by the spread of radioactive wastes across the landscape. After the immediate danger is over, the thought of such a tragedy lingers and weakens the confidence of the public in the peaceful uses of atomic energy. For example, there is no doubt that we need to replace coal- and oil-fired electric generating stations with nuclear power plants. And this replacement needs to take place in and around cities if for no other reason than to reduce air pollution. Advances in technology make it evident that nuclear power is an effective way of generating electricity. But public acceptance has not been very enthusiastic. In fact, the first proposal Consolidated Edison made to build an atomic plant in New York City raised a storm of protest. The proposed site was at Ravenswood in Queens. Con Edison dropped the idea and found alternate sources for electric power in Canada.

In 1970, Con Edison operated a nuclear plant on the Hudson River at Indian Point near Peekskill. Other sites along the Hudson are appropriate and are being considered as locations for nuclear generating stations. A four-million-kilowatt plant is proposed for David's Island, the site of old Fort Slocum, off New Rochelle. Probably the first site within New York City is slated to be on Welfare Island in the East River. The problem, of course, is to acquaint the public with the safety and reliability records being achieved in the operation of nuclear plants. But the other side of the coin demands that every precaution be taken to insure safety.

It does not take much of an eye for beauty to realize that the condition of our landscape is appalling. The most obvious blights are the dreary billboards, highway signs, and hamburger-stand architecture that line many highways between towns. And, within the city limits, the sights that spread before us are not much better.

There is no doubt, in my mind, that many or most commercial signs along a highway, parkway, turnpike, or freeway represent a hazard to its safe use by motorists. Thus, serviceability, safety, and the scenic qualities of the roadway are affected. Zoning and billboard control are the answer. I shall never understand the reluctance to use these means to clear the blight.

The parade of the utility power lines across the landscape is more understandable. After all, these power lines did bring civilization to remote areas. But the clutter of poles and lines in our cities and towns is inexcusable today. A new emphasis on burying utility lines has been developing. The year 1975 has been proposed as a date after which no new overhead lines are to be constructed in new residential subdivisions. And each year an increasing number of power lines have been going underground. The utilities will have about one billion dollars invested in underground lines by 1975. But this is a mere pittance compared to the investments that will need to be made to bury all existing power lines. The figure to accomplish the task is estimated at more than 150 billion dollars.

The existing overhead lines cost about eighteen billion dollars. The spread of electric power in the United States was accomplished quickly and rather cheaply. Now the problem is to redo the wiring in order to unclutter the landscape. It is going to be an expensive task. We cannot expect utility companies to do the job out of current profits, because these are controlled by

Billboards and highway signs without end.

our watchdog committees. Massive federal assistance is going to be needed. It will be money well spent. But on top of this we need to improve the utility companies' profit structure so that they are in a better financial position to undertake some of these tasks that are in the public interest. A simple 4 percent income tax credit based on the company's investment in distribution facilities would give them an opportunity to do the job themselves.

The most annoying aspect of landscape pollution is the collection of trash, tin cans, and automobiles strewn hither and yon. Each year we dispose of almost fifty billion cans of one kind or another. And most people are not too careful about this littering, which you can find strewn on beaches, streets, or in the water. More than twenty-five billion bottles and jars also become a disposal problem, with many finding their way to roadside havens.

Open-face mine land is another scar on the landscape that takes a long time to heal. Giant swatches of scarred earth are created by this kind of mining operation. More that two million acres of land have been destroyed in this way. With few exceptions, the companies responsible have refused to restore the land and erase the havoc created by their mining operations.

There is still plenty of land in the United States. And it is possible to have a much greater population density. We are not crowded on a body-per-acre basis even in our larger cities, even though slums have too many bodies per room. Our problem is proper utilization of land. We have been developing land that should be left to nature, as in the Everglades and on its borders. And in other cases we have been hoarding land that should be used. We need intelligent land-use planning.

Jersey City, New Jersey, for example, is a city with a 350-year history. And yet, one-fifth of its land was considered underdeveloped in 1969. New Orleans, Newark, Syracuse, and St. Louis have similar problems.

The National Commission on Urban Problems reported that at the end of the 1960s unimproved land makes up about one-third of all private holdings in urban areas of one hundred thousand or more population. This seems almost unbelievable. But in the "typical" city of this size, for each 10,000 residents, 218 acres is devoted to public streets, 158 acres is devoted to

Litter in our gutters is much too common a sight.

Automobiles piled one on top of the other are a rather common sight in our society.

public and semipublic uses, 443 acres to private residential property, and 139 acres to commercial, industrial, and railroad property, while some 269 *acres remain as undeveloped private land.*

Even among the big cities with populations of more than 250,000, an average of 12.5 percent of the land was undeveloped. Almost one-third of the land in these cities is publicly owned. Streets and highways generally occupy from one-sixth to one-fourth of city areas. Less than one-third of the land in these cities is used for residential purposes. Commercial, industrial, and railroad uses occupy from 8 to 16 percent of the land.

Our concern for land use must also extend to the forests, the countryside, and even underground. For example, a sixteen-hundred-foot well was used by a paper mill in Pennsylvania to dispose of waste. Nontoxic pulping liquors formed by paper mill processes were injected into a huge limestone layer sixteen hundred feet beneath the ground. Many wells have been dug for such purposes. Often, poisonous waste products disposed of in this way have caused ground contamination.

In 1969, there were 110 deep wells throughout the United States. These wells were being used for the disposal of sulphuric acid from steel mills, as well as of pharmaceutical and chemical wastes. A uranium installation in New Mexico was pumping nuclear waste (including radium-226) into a deep well. Most of the wastes disposed of in this way were poisons, but the radium-226 will remain dangerous for thousands of years. Unbelievably small traces of radium-226 in drinking water cause bone damage. And no one knows for sure where waste products will go once they are sent down a disposal well.

At times, wastes pumped underground cause more than just contamination. Denver, for example, may be threatened by a manmade earthquake as a result of 160 million gallons of poisonous water being pumped underground. The United States Army's Rocky Mountain Arsenal outside Denver drilled a two-mile-deep well. They poured poisonous water, a by-product of chemical-warfare research, down the well. The weight of the water opened fissures in the rock, and this caused tremors. The water has more than likely caused movement in an unstable rock formation deep below Denver. It is very difficult to rectify

This junkyard operator keeps things neat by setting a match to the trash. The soot and ash, of course, will take flight and come to rest somewhere down the road. Cities, too, must be concerned about the purposes for which land is used.

or correct such a situation once it develops. The waste pumped below ground is not replacing other liquids; it is adding to them. This changes the fluid pressure deep within the earth.

The planning of land use must be undertaken with great care and caution. Any plan may affect natural balances and, eventually, the condition of the entire earth. Consider, for example, the plan concerning the Arctic proposed by the Russian meteorologist, Dr. M. J. Budyko. The Russian scientist suggested that by ridding the Arctic of its ice, a mild climate would prevail over the region. Temperature differences between the equator and the poles are largely due to the ice, not to differences in solar radiation. Dr. Budyko's studies indicate that once the ice is destroyed, it would not return. The ice cover, he contends, is the cause, not the result of the low temperatures in the high latitudes. Vegetation of the Temperate Zone could thrive in the area.

But what are the consequences of the Russian plan? Changes in weather, climate, level of the sea, vegetation, and animal life would certainly occur. Are they the changes we want? Can we live with them? Can we survive under the new conditions?

Zambia is the world's third-largest producer of copper. Located in south-central Africa on a plateau four thousand feet above sea level, it has no access to the sea, and much of its soil is poor. In the past, its economy has been completely dependent on copper.

In 1968, the World Bank approved loans totaling sixteen million dollars to help Zambia launch a forestry project and to rebuild a road linking its copper-producing area with a Tanzanian port. The forestry project is intended to provide the African country with fast-growing, high-yielding wood species. The forestry project can help reduce the dependence of the country on imported wood. It is also a step in the direction of wise land use and an attempt to diversify the activity within the country.

The population of Zambia, in 1968, was about 3,900,000. By the mid-1970s, the population will, more than likely, be approaching five million. The first concern of any developing country is its economic growth. Sacrifices are often made to attract and retain industry. Under such circumstances, industry often exploits the natural environment in the interest of rapid growth and rapid return on its investment.

This procedure of exploitation was the rule in the early development of the United States. Most lumbering interests, for example, ravished the virgin timberlands and cut trees indiscriminately. Only after great damage was done to the forests of the United States did the lumber companies develop a more enlightened procedure of selective cutting and replanting. The strip miners and the copper interests also scarred the land with their shovels and with the pollution from their smelters.

The damage done by the exploiters is slowly being repaired in the United States. And, today, enlightened companies in lumbering and mining are making land reclamation an integral part of the production process. Mine operators especially need to look ahead and to decide what the reclaimed land will be used for—agriculture, recreation, or real estate development. For example, rock removal leaves pits that can become lakes. Then, when the land is used for residential purposes, each home can have its own lakefront. Some of the phosphate companies in Florida, for example, are greatly involved in agriculture. Much of the reclaimed land is ideal for new citrus groves.

Reclamation programs give a company almost total land use. The lesson for the world is that the reclamation programs now used in highly developed countries ought to be used from the start, as industry and mining operations develop, in the so-called underdeveloped countries of the world.

The sun is beginning to rise from among the clouds hanging over Marti-
nique. The sailing ship, gently nudged by the wind, makes its way slowly
to this port in the Caribbean Sea.

Chapter 8

THE ENDLESS SEA

One way of viewing the earth is as one huge ocean, which is broken here and there by islands that we call continents. The ocean, in fact, covers about three-fourths of the earth's surface. This water surface—the ocean—is never still. Waves constantly roll to shore, gently on a calm day but with a heavy, pounding thud when driven by a howling wind.

The sea is filled with life. Fish dart hither and yon in search of food, in pursuit of other fish, or at times to escape larger enemies. Animals of all shapes and sizes move through the waters. Often, you find some of the life cast upon the shore. Shells and seaweed dot almost any beach that you stroll along.

Into this ever-moving ocean pours the waste from the lands. Man and nature contribute a share. Salts, silt, sand, and rock wash from the land, making the sea water more salty and building layers of muck and ooze at its bottom. Man dumps trash, garbage, oil, radioactive materials, and other wastes with the simple belief that it will be swallowed forever by the vast, swirling ocean. We have acted as if there is no limit to what the ocean waters can absorb. We see evidence of this limit, however, in the pollution of tidal estuaries and beaches. We are confronted with a serious problem, which can no longer be ignored.

The Pacific, the Atlantic, and the Indian Oceans really form one continuous body of water, which can be called the *world ocean*. In the Southern Hemisphere, these oceans come together and form what is called the *Antarctic Ocean*. The Pacific and Atlantic meet in the Northern Hemisphere to form the Arctic Ocean.

Each of these oceans includes smaller bodies of water: bays, gulfs, and seas. Thus, in the Atlantic you have the Irish Sea, the Caribbean Sea, the Bay of Biscay, and the Gulf of Mexico, to mention only a few of the subdivisions.

The Pacific covers about 63.8 million square miles. This is more than one-third of the surface of the earth. The average depth in this ocean is about 14,000 feet; but the deepest location, the Challenger Deep, is 36,198 feet.

The chief industrial countries of the world lie along the coasts of the Atlantic Ocean. Its waters cover about 31.5 million square miles of the earth's surface. The average depth of the Atlantic is the same as that of the Pacific, 14,000 feet; but its deepest point, the Milwaukee Deep, is only 27,498 feet.

The Indian Ocean covers an area of slightly more than 28.3 million square miles. It is the smallest of the three great oceans. Its average depth is about 13,000 feet; and the deepest spot, south of the island of Java, is about 25,000 feet.

The waters of the ocean contain, on the average, about 3.5 percent salts. Sodium, calcium, and magnesium salts are included. But realize that all the elements found in the earth's crust are also found in sea water. Temperatures of the surface water range from about 28° F in the polar regions to about 86° F in the tropics. The great area covered by the world ocean and the great quantity of water serve to regulate and control the earth's climate.

We know relatively little about the oceans. It has only been since the mid-1960s that scientists have been given sufficient grants of money to undertake the enormous job of research that needs to be done. New equipment and new techniques for probing the oceans are now available.

Three kinds of ocean research vessels are being used: above-surface ships, mobile submarines, and deep-diving bathyscaphes. Today, efficient surface ships are designed with very specialized scientific equipment for oceanographic research. This is quite a change from the reconverted tankers and freighters that were used in the early days. The mobile submarines have their own special design, which allows them to probe nooks and crannies across the continental shelves. Deep diving is done in the spherical, thick-hulled bathyscaphes.

There are also other types of oceanographic research ships. Flip is one of these. It is 355 feet long, and it literally flips up on

In this fish-eye view we see a specialist in underwater photography observing an oil slick that is beginning to break up as a result of an application of oil dispersant. As the slick begins to disperse, sunlight begins to filter through the cleared water.

end. The lower, tubular part forms an immersed, vertical laboratory, which can be used to collect all kinds of data.

Maps of the ocean floor are very crude. Approximately 3 percent of the ocean floor actually has been mapped. Thus we know very little about a very substantial part of the earth. In fact, at the end of the 1960s, we knew more about the surface of the moon than we did about the ocean floor. We are only beginning to learn how interesting the seascape of the ocean is.

Most gasoline today contains tetraethyl lead. With every revolution of an automobile's internal combustion engine, poisonous lead is exhausted into the atmosphere. Some five hundred thousand tons of this lead are carried into the oceans of the Northern Hemisphere each year.

Tetraethyl lead was first added to gasoline about thirty-five years ago. It is used to prevent knocking, or pinging, in the internal combustion engine. Prior to its use in gasoline, the only lead that washed into the ocean was from rock weathering. About ten thousand tons of lead are added to the oceans each year by the process of weathering. Today, rain washes about three hundred thousand tons, consisting of small particles of lead oxide, out of the atmosphere into the oceans. Another two hundred thousand tons moves into the sea from the rivers. The lead carried by the rivers comes from automobile exhausts and from industrial plants. And a small portion of the river lead comes, as it always did, from the weathering of rock on the land.

Lead is widely distributed over the earth. It is the decay end-product of radioactive minerals and, therefore, is found in rocks. Lead should normally be one of the rarest elements in ocean water; however, it is losing this status because of the increasing rate at which it is being spewed into the oceans by automobile emissions. The rate at the end of the 1960s was more than fifty times the natural rate to be expected from the weathering of rock.

What are the consequences of the buildup of lead in the oceans? No one knows! But it may be disturbing the fishes and other marine life in ways that we cannot yet imagine. It may also be upsetting the geochemical cycle in the oceans. The heaviest concentrations of lead appear to be at the water's surface.

Lead, of course, is only one of many pollutants moving into the oceans. The real problem of predicting the consequences of these pollutants is that we have very little reliable data on what is really happening. The United States set up, during 1968, its first service to help predict how rapidly river-water pollutants were being washed out to sea. A pilot program was operated during that year at the Penobscot River and Bay Estuary in Maine. The Penobscot, during the 1960s, was heavily polluted from industries such as paper mills. It should be clear that one pilot program is insufficient. We should at this point in time be much farther along in collecting data than is the case when you are tinkering with a pilot program.

The beach gets its share of waste. Driftwood washes to shore and settles there along with the beer cans, boxes, and other debris carried there by people on outings.

Suspended in the oceans are vast supplies of sodium, calcium, sulphur, magnesium, boron, cobalt, iodine, vanadium, gold, and silver. More than 166 million tons of dissolved salts float in one cubic mile of ocean water. The problem that perplexes the engineers is how to extract this wealth in an economical way. Possibly, the solution of the future will be to recover these rich minerals from the desalination plants that are currently being used to convert sea water to fresh water.

The ocean bed, at the present time, is open to colonization and exploitation just as the North American, South American, and African continents were at an earlier time. The promise of future profits to industry and economic power to the successful nations is not unlike the lure that brought England, France, and Spain into conflict in North America. And we may see national rivalries develop on the ocean floor. What is needed today, however, is not a large navy and willing colonists, but a technology that will allow men to live in the ocean and to extract its riches. The sea is the last area on earth open to free exploitation by those with the scientific capability. The fear that has been expressed is that excesses may be committed in this exploitation that will unleash changes that will affect the whole earth— especially its climate and the life within the sea.

The wealth of the sea that we presently remove is food: fish, lobsters, mussels, clams, crabs, and edible seaweed. Fish of all sorts and descriptions are taken by ships of all nations. Fishermen have exploited the sea and have not been concerned about harvesting in limited amounts. The exploitation of the whale is a classic example of the butchering that took place with little thought to conservation.

Whatever man eventually determines to do with the ocean, we must remember that there is a chain of life that must be respected and preserved. The green pastures of microscopic sea plants are the first part of the chain. Some fifteen thousand different kinds of delicate cells drift with the wind and currents and serve as food for the tiny sea animals called zooplankton. These microscopic animals are, in turn, eaten by small fish such as herring and sardines. Larger fish feed on the smaller fish, and so it goes in a ruthless succession of life feeding on life. Bacteria also play a part in this complex chain. The bacteria

Asherah is a research submarine equipped with stereo cameras. Many geological studies have been undertaken with this submarine.

release nutritious phosphates, nitrates, and silicates into the sea from the remains of plants and animals that sink toward the bottom.

Ocean mining currently is confined mostly to sulphur, diamonds, sand, and gravel. About sixty million dollars' worth of products were taken from the sea in 1969. But even when minerals are found, it is often very expensive to move them, as, for example, with the large manganese deposits discovered in nodule form on the ocean floor. The main obstacle to mining the manganese at the present time is the cost of gathering them. The same economics prevents mining globules of copper and nickel that can be found on the ocean bottom at depths of eighteen thousand and twenty thousand feet.

There appears to be vast reservoirs of oil and gas under the sea. Many wells have been drilled to tap into these pools. In fact, in 1968, some 13 percent of the domestic oil production in the United States came from offshore wells. The offshore production (until the North Slope strike in Alaska) was growing more than four times as fast as onshore production.

There are many difficulties, however, in tapping undersea reservoirs of oil and gas. Great depths of water mean greater costs and more difficulty. It may be many years before deep-water oil is fully exploited, especially since there is the prospect of easier access to reserves on the North Slope. But exploration is continuing. In 1968 some eighteen million dollars were spent in exploration of Canadian offshore waters alone by oil and gas companies.

A well in the North Sea about 150 miles off the coast of Norway brought in sizable amounts of natural gas and natural gas liquids, a condensate that resembles crude oil. It is the first discovery of oil or gas off Norway. The liquid discovery is unusual for the North Sea. The previous wells in the North Sea have been gas wells. The first well produced forty million cubic feet of natural gas and more than two thousand barrels of oil daily.

The search for deep-water gas and oil is under way all over the earth. In 1968, exploration started off the eastern seaboard of the United States. The offshore area being surveyed runs from Virginia to two hundred miles east of Massachusetts. It is larger than the combined Gulf Coast continental shelf of Texas and Louisiana. The search area includes two geologic basins: the Baltimore Canyon and Georges Bank. The Baltimore Canyon is parallel to the Delaware-New Jersey coast. Georges Bank is parallel to the Rhode Island-southern Massachusetts coast.

What does all this mean? It means that we may begin seeing drilling platforms and wells rising from the most unlikely places. And we had better be alert to whether proper safeguards are being employed in the drilling operations, or the east coast of the United States may face a tragedy.

Oceangoing tankers are being used to transport oil to all parts of the world. Jersey Standard alone has a fleet of 105 tankers. These tankers carry fantastic amounts of crude oil. In 1970, sixty-one tankers were in the one hundred thousand to two hundred thousand dead-weight tonnage range; twenty-seven ships were larger than two hundred thousand tons, and six were even larger than three hundred thousand tons. Dead-weight tonnage rating of a ship tells us how many tons of oil it can carry.

A helicopter is being used to spray a dispersant on an oil slick. The slick can be seen dispersing to the rear. For oil slick dispersion, helicopters are useful in hard-to-reach areas close to a shoreline. Their prop wash can provide a mixing energy or turbulence that produces most effective results.

In recent years, there have been a number of spectacular disasters that sent millions of gallons of oil into the sea. One of the famous episodes was the breaking of the oil tanker *Torrey Canyon* on a rock near Land's End, England. More than 118,000 tons of crude oil poured into the sea and moved relentlessly onto the English beaches. Disasters, such as that of the *Torrey Canyon*, were given wide publicity by the press, but each year, during the decade from 1958 to 1968, about five tankers were lost.

When oil spills into the sea close to shore, people feel compelled to do something about it. And the English are no exception to the rule. During the spring of 1967, various attempts were made to dissipate the oil from the *Torrey Canyon*. The Royal Air Force bombed the hulking tanker in an attempt to burn the floating oil. The lighter components of the oil did burn, but then the fire went out, leaving the blackest, stickiest, messiest part of the oil to float onto the resort beaches in the area. Cleanup squads sprayed detergents along the coast as a last resort to break up the oil. The oil simply covered the beaches of Cornwall and was not affected by the detergents.

Thousands of sea birds died from being coated with oil or from swallowing it. The stench and unsightly condition of beaches and harbors were unbelievable. The long-term effect of the oil on the ecology of the region will not be known for years. The detergents used to combat the oil had more immediate and more direct effect on the marine life than did the oil. A significant amount of marine life was killed by the detergents. Plants by the thousands were destroyed or stunted. The populations of lobster, shrimp, and crabs on one reef was almost totally wiped out. Starfish and sea urchins on the same reef completely disappeared.

Limpets and other browsing creatures live in the tidal zone. The activity of these animals keeps the shoreline free of decayed material and controls the growth of seaweed. The detergents significantly reduced the number of tidal zone animals. The ecology, or balance, between plants and animals was seriously upset in most of the coastal areas. Vivid proof of the ecological upset came the next year, when portions of the Cornwall coast were overgrown with seaweed.

Each year more tankers are built and pressed into service. In 1968, fifteen tankers were under construction or on order at the Sparrows Point, Maryland, shipyard of Bethlehem Steel Corporation. And remember, this is only one shipyard; tankers are being built throughout the world. In all likelihood, tankers will be used to transport crude oil from Alaska to West and East Coast ports of the United States as a result of the development of the North Slope oil fields. Each time a tanker embarks on a journey, there is the danger of catastrophe. With the increase in the size of tankers, the dimensions of the tragedy and damage that can occur to the plants, the animals, and the waters of the ocean increase, too. There is a need to institute new safeguards in the construction as well as in the navigation of these huge tankers.

The tug is pushing a tanker into position for loading at the Arabian American Oil Company's Ras Tanura Marine Terminal in Saudi Arabia.

All ships sailing the oceans put waste material into the sea. Most of the tanker-connected sea pollution during ordinary operations results when tanks are cleaned after the oil cargo is discharged. The tanks are usually cleaned at sea. Water is used to flush the tanks, and the oil-water emulsion that results is then discharged into the sea.

The amount of oil-water emulsion is insignificant for a single tanker. The bacteria in the ocean would be able to handle the task of utilizing and destroying the oil. But think of the world fleet of tankers, which transports nine hundred million tons of oil across the oceans of the world in one year! The stream of oil flushed from all these tanks is a sizable amount.

Ballast water is also a problem. It is taken into the same tanks in which the oil is being, or has been, transported. Thus a certain amount of the ballast water becomes contaminated with oil. The only way to avoid this is to have separate tanks for ballast and for the oil cargo. Ballast keeps the ship from bobbing along the top of the sea like a cork. It also serves to prevent structural damage to the ship from the pounding of the waves. Usually, ballast make up about one-third of the dead-weight tonnage (the amount of cargo a ship can hold). Thus, for a ship with a dead-weight tonnage of seventy-one-thousand, the ballast may be as much as twenty-four thousand tons. As a tanker approaches port, it usually flushes the dirty ballast into the sea and takes on clean sea water. Then the so-called clean ballast is dumped into the harbor as new cargo is taken on.

The main pollution-producing materials discharged from tankers are the "persistent oils." These oils, crude and heavy fuel oils, are not easily consumed by the bacteria in the ocean. Tanker captains should be instructed to abstain completely from discharging oily water into the sea. Oily residues from ballast water and from flushing tanks should be discharged at the refinery or the terminal. Then various methods can be used to remove the oil and process the water before it is returned to any waterway or to the sea.

Oil in underground reservoirs often leaks, or seeps, to the surface. In fact, the first oil discoveries were natural seeps. Some of the natural seepage on land moves into streams and rivers. There is also natural seepage at sea from underground reservoirs. At least seven natural seeps have been located in the Caribbean Sea. Two natural seeps off the California coast are adding significant amounts of oil to the ocean water.

Approximately 103 tankers were sunk off the United States coast during World War II. These hulks are rotting and constitute a serious threat as a potential source of pollution of the ocean waters off the U.S. coast. Oil seeps from the tanks of these sunken ships. After years in the water, any one of the tankers can break up dramatically and release its cargo into the sea. About five million barrels of oil are still in these sunken tankers. This amounts to over two hundred million gallons of oil.

Any ship, however, is a possible source of sea pollution. The bilge serves as a collection point for oil leaks from all over the ship. When the bilges are cleaned, this material is sent into the sea. The fuel bunker tanks of all ships are cleaned periodically, too. These wastes are discharged into the sea.

Every little bit helps—helps to pollute, that is! All waste puts a strain on the natural cleansing activities of bacteria in the sea. The wastes may become so burdensome that we may overwhelm the oceans just as we have overwhelmed our rivers and lakes. The time for positive control action is now.

An intact oil slick is a danger to animal life. It represents a barrier to the transfer of oxygen from the atmosphere to the water to support the marine life. The animals also become fouled with the oil. In addition, birds living in or around the oil slick also become fouled.

A plastic foam material (polyurethane foam) has proven to be valuable in cleaning up oil slicks. The plastic material looks like white bread and is shredded and then sprayed on an oil slick. Floating booms consisting of a small bore net are used to contain the oil until it is adsorbed by the foam, much like a sponge adsorbs water. The booms are then towed to a place where the foam containing the oil is scooped up. This procedure is economical and allows us to recover 80 percent of the oil by pressing the foam.

In 1968, the Esso Research and Engineering Company developed a spray product that disperses oil slicks and promotes the natural disintegration of the oil. This spray is not like the detergents that produce widespread damage to marine life. This new spray, called Corexit, can be used without harming fish or other marine life. Shrimp are particularly sensitive to any kind of pollutant and, thus, they were used in the tests to determine the safety of Corexit. This chemical acts as a dispersant that speeds up the spreading process and breaks the slick into small droplets. The droplets as a result of Corexit's action are unable

In areas where the use of aircraft may not be considered feasible, large-scale applications can be made from workboats using spray booms. Dispersion of the oil can be clearly seen here. The spray boom shown is a portable one specifically designed by Enjay Chemical Company for spraying its Corexit oil dispersant. It is designed for surface application. This portable boom can also be used on planes and helicopters.

to form a slick again. The final decomposition of the dispersed oil takes place by natural processes—mainly bacterial action.

An estimated forty million people are boating in the United States. About 90 percent of the 8.5 million pleasure boats are equipped with sanitation facilities and will discharge untreated wastes into navigable waters. Antipollution devices ought to be added to the marine sanitary facilities on all boats. Some sort of maceration and/or chlorination device to treat human waste before discharge is needed.

Fish can become infected with human disease germs by exposure to water that is contaminated by human wastes. More than two hundred white perch caught in rivers that flow through heavily populated areas into Chesapeake Bay were tested and

Rotting piers, barges, and ships contribute to the driftwood and debris in harbors.

found to contain antibodies to the bacteria that cause human pseudotuberculosis, paratyphoid fever, vacillary dysentery, and a variety of chronic infections. Heavy contamination of our waters causes natural purification processes to fail and can establish a human-to-fish-human chain of infection.

The problem of floating debris in most of the harbors of the world is serious. A fantastic amount of dead trees and other wood comes down most rivers after heavy rains. The debris makes its way through the bays and into the sea. Old rotting ships, barges, and piers are another source of drift and debris. In New York Harbor alone, more than six hundred thousand cubic feet of driftwood and similar material are collected each year. On the average, this amounts to 62,500 tons of debris a day. The collection of this debris in the harbor is a costly operation. But it is one that must be done, because the debris menaces boats moving through the harbor. More than one-half million dollars a year is spent to collect and incinerate it.

A sewer pipe that ends on a beach is frightening. What kind of water is discharged from it?

How long will man use the ocean as a sewer into which he sends his refuse? The driftwood is only one very visible example of what is coming down our rivers, through our bays, and into our oceans. Slime, muck, and sewage, most of it invisible, rushes down the Hudson and most of the other rivers throughout the world—with very few exceptions.

In the past, man has used the oceans as a supposedly unlimited sink into which he dumped refuse from coastal communities and certain industrial operations. Methods of disposal have ranged from merely hauling the waste to sea and dumping it, to subjecting the waste to some treatment before dumping. Radioactive wastes were, at one time, placed in vaults and taken to sea for deep burial. Results were not very satisfactory.

Dumping at sea seems to me to be another version of the objectionable open dump. It is, of course, a marine version! A good portion of the wastes, for example, dumped from garbage barges fails to sink. Eventually this putrid material is washed

You can find cans, bottles, and other debris in most waters where boats anchor.

up on a beach. Then we not only have pollution of the sea, but of the land as well.

Recently there have been proposals to compress garbage so that it is dense enough to sink when dumped into the ocean. Even if it is possible to compress garbage to a density of 66.5 pounds per cubic foot, there is a real question of how long the treated material will remain submerged in the sea. Decomposition will certainly take place, and gas will form. Bales of garbage under such circumstances will swell and break open. Some of the material will float to the surface. Then there is also the question as to what effect and influence the submerged garbage will have on the plants and animals of the immediate environment, as well as on the condition of the sea water. The volume of wastes produced throughout the world is staggering. No plan for disposal of any portion of these wastes in the sea should be implemented without careful scrutiny of the consequences.

Chapter 9

POLLUTION AND POLITICS

No simple statement can be made about the environment and man's relationship to it. The need to regulate our activity and to prevent the fouling of the environment is obvious. The fact of the matter is that the establishment and maintenance of a healthy environment is not primarily a technical problem. Our science is adequate to accomplish the task. We have the technical tools which, if applied, can correct the situation. Our inadequacies lie in the area of social awareness, political skill, and economic planning. Environmental control is a social, political, and economic problem.

Today, we are faced with centuries of man's misuse and abuse of the environment. And even though we recognize the difficulty, no improvement is made because the social, political, and economic tools we use are insufficient. Jurisdictional disagreements linger and fester. Crowded court calendars, inadequate legislation, and judicial opinion rooted in the past handicap those who act responsibly to protect the environment.

During the 1960s, Jersey City in Hudson County, New Jersey, was locked in legal combat with the citizens of Morris County. Claim and counterclaim, old contracts and new, interpretations of law; and most people began to forget that the real issue was quality drinking water for hundreds of thousands of people and the accompanying pollution of the Rockaway and Passaic Rivers. Read for yourself the article written by a staff reporter of the *Jersey Journal* in the August 28, 1968 issue of that newspaper:

The Jersey City versus Morris County dispute over sewage treatment and the accompanying problem of pollution of the Rockaway and Passaic rivers continues to rage today, with no solution in sight.

Jersey City has won a round of sorts, in the form of a court decision banning nine Morris communities from issuing building permits or certificates of occupancy for any structures which would feed their sewage into the rivers.

We have an unquenchable thirst for power to run our factories and homes. The use of water to produce this power is a step in the right direction. But it, too, has been surrounded by controversy. The government becomes involved in the building of dams and selling the power. Then there is also the problem of drowning many millions of acres of land with the waters of the reservoir that accumulate behind the dam or a reservoir. This view shows Hoover Dam.

However, this does not alleviate the problem of Jersey City's overburdened sewage treatment plant, built in Morris County in return for potable water rights. And, besides curtailing the area's building boom, the order does not solve the communities' overall sewage disposal problem.

To make sense of the situation, to find out how it happened to come to a head the way it did, it is necessary to dredge the facts documenting the hostility between the Morris County municipalities and Jersey City.

Back in 1903, Jersey City took steps to assure a dependable source of water for its residents. The decision was made at that time to switch from using water from the Passaic River and to construct a reservoir of its own.

As a result, the Jersey City Water Works Reservoir was created in Boonton and water from the Rockaway River watershed area was impounded in this storage basin.

In return for permission to use the reservoir site for storage of its water, Jersey City made agreements with the communities in that area of Morris County at that time.

So, in 1921, plans were prepared by Jersey City engineers to intercept raw sewage from the towns of Dover, Boonton, Rockaway Borough, Wharton and Denville, which bordered the watershed.

These towns agreed to run sewer laterals into the 11.5 mile trunk sewer completed in 1925 by Jersey City, along with its companion sewage treatment plant.

Although in 1921 five municipalities were anticipating hooking into the Jersey City treatment system, by the time the plant was completed, only Dover and the Borough of Rockaway had signed contracts with Jersey City.

Both contracts were drawn up for a forty-year period with the understanding that they would continue to be valid ". . . as much longer as the waters herein mentioned (Rockaway River) are used for potable purposes."

Dover was the earliest signer in May, 1918, and Rockaway Borough followed suit in September, 1924. The borough penned another agreement in March, 1934, as a supplement to the original, when federal aid was being given to the town for revision of its sewer lines.

Boonton entered the system in 1931 with an agreement similar if not identical to the contracts issued previously.

In May, 1954, the Wharton Sewerage Authority made arrangements to connect into the trunk sewer running from Wharton to Boonton after an unexplainable lapse of nearly a quarter of a century.

In preparation for this hookup, Jersey City issued building contracts for the enlargement of its sewage-treatment plant at a cost of more than $1 million. The renovation was completed in October, 1953, in time for Wharton's entry.

The wording of the contract made with Wharton this time did not include any mention of a time period or of the use of the Rockaway River as Jersey City's water supply source. The key words in this contract are that Jersey City will be responsible for the treatment of Wharton's sewage ". . . in consideration of the mutual advantages to be derived by each of the parties."

At any rate, no matter what the contract said, the plant was now capable of handling a daily average of 5.4 million gallons. And the communities involved in treatment procedures agree that the plant functioned up to maximum capacity perfectly.

The only other town included in the original plans for sewer hook-ups, Denville, entered the system one year earlier than Wharton in September, 1953. Its contract contained the same wording as that of the contract signed with Wharton.

However, apparently the only way Denville was able to edge its way into the system was by pointing out it was looking for a means of eliminating itself as a source of pollution to the Rockaway River.

Eleven years later, the town was compelled to draw up another contract which stated: "Whereas no provision for payment was made in the aforesaid agreement and whereas there has been a steadily increasing flow of population, we have requested the township of Denville to pay a portion of the costs and whereas Denville takes the position that the right of the city to make these charges is a legal issue . . . then Denville shall pay 8 cents per 1000 gallons treated."

Rockaway Township came in as the seventh municipality for the same reason: its sewage as well was causing pollution of the Rockaway River. So in June, 1954, consent was given for the township to hook into the system with language identical to those of Wharton and Denville.

Randolph Township became the last of the towns to enter into agreements with Jersey City for sewage treatment. The township was also compelled to pay for a portion of the treatment, the price being the same as for Denville.

Jersey City has made no agreement with either Boonton Township or with Victory Gardens, the former involving only the Board of Education or the schools which tie into the system, and the latter being a 200-family unit, an area which was utilized during World War II to house the staff of the Picatinny Arsenal.

Randolph and Rockaway Townships connect into the sewer laterals of Dover. Dover charges $175 as the initial cost for each connection and $5 annually for a maintenance fee. There are 1,000 connections made in Dover.

Today, the Jersey City plant, allegedly understaffed and not maintained up to capacity, is not able to handle, the State Board of Health contends, the amount of sewage it ingests.

This plant ". . . must be improved, altered, or added to on or before October 30, 1970, in accordance with the order by the State Board of Health."

This wording leaves the door open to any type of indefinite renovation for the Parsippany treatment plant. While the money Jersey City is investing will cover only the costs for a "primary" repair, a "tertiary" repair is envisioned by residents of the area.

However, the towns bordering the watershed area expect Jersey City to pay the full cost for a tertiary plant. Or at least they maintain that Jersey City is obligated to carry the full burden of the expenses.

Technically, they are right, but as the state has forcefully suggested, these municipalities must come to grips ultimately with the problem of treatment of more and more sewage each year.

Several of the contracts use the wording "in consideration of the mutual advantages to be derived by each of the parties." Clearly, it is not to Jersey City's advantage to be compelled to continue to take care of Morris County's problems.

The suggestion to consider the formation of a regional sewage authority has fallen on deaf ears, except for a few Parsippany councilmen. The rest of Morris County's officials are content to let Jersey City come up with the solution.

And apparently, Jersey City officials are reciprocating in the same manner. Both sides to the dispute claim that neither made an effort to follow up informal discussions on ways and means to renegotiate the contracts or to reach agreement on sharing the cost on a more equal level for sewage treatment.

All of the former talk and attempt at establishing good will can only come to naught if the bickering continues. Probably two main factors contributed to making the situation what it now is.

First, the contracts between Morris County muncipalities and Jersey City make provisions only for the treatment of domestic and sanitary sewage, not storm sewage. Undoubtedly, the excess volume of water from heavy rainfalls was responsible, over the years, for a portion of the extra load not anticipated with the plant's design.

Secondly, leaks have been discovered somewhere in the sewer

system. The towns have tentatively agreed to conduct infiltration studies to determine the source of the leakage which constitutes about 2 million gallons of excess water to be treated by the plant.

What kind of reasonableness needs to be brought to such disputes? We must assume that there were and are reasonable people in Jersey City and Morris County. What kept them from solving the problem for so many years? Whose negligence was involved? What kinds of social conscience, political skills, and economic realities operate to prevent a solution that all must recognize to be in the interest of maintaining community and area health?

Real progress in pollution control can only come when the gravity of the problem is recognized by each one of us. The next step is to have adequate laws passed and executed at both the national and state levels. The fact that laws exist and can be enforced is evident when you again turn to the pages of local newspapers. In this case, the *Jersey Journal* reported the following story during 1968:

Koppers, a Kearny fuel company, was fined $10,000 in Hudson County Superior Court on an air pollution complaint from the State Health Department.

The fine was levied against the Koppers Company, Inc., by Superior Court Judge Robert A. Matthews.

Deputy Atty. Gen. Theodore A. Schwartz, who prosecuted the case, said after the hearing that this was one of the largest fines he could recall being levied against a firm on an air pollution charge.

During the hearing, the Koppers lawyer, Francis X. Journick, said the firm was trying to comply with state regulations and was installing $500,000 worth of equipment to make the necessary adjustments.

The court extended by six months a restraint order, during which the company must complete installation of the equipment.

In the past, the firm has paid fines ranging from $25 to $1,500 for violations.

We also find that state antipollution laws are being contested by certain companies. This evidence is found in the Sunday Newark *Star-Ledger* of January 5, 1969:

A major test case on the constitutionality of the State of New Jersey laws against air pollution will be heard by the State Supreme Court.

The appeal is being staged by the Owens Corning Fiberglass Corporation, which operates a $1.2 million plant in the Camden County community of Burlington.

In 1967, the State Department of Health, after six years of proceedings with the company, ordered the concern to eliminate allegedly objectionable odors which were affecting three communities.

The Superior Court Appellate Division upheld that ruling in a voluminous opinion last May. Now the highest court of the state is reviewing the legal dispute.

The legal challenge centers on the state's 1954 law permitting the health department to enact regulations based on standards contained in the law and the 1961 code establishing the regulations.

In general, each chapter of the 1961 code deals with specific types of pollutants, such as smoke from fuel burning and sulphur compounds, but Chapter 6 is a "catch-all" provision governing all general emissions that can be hazardous or "interfere with comfortable living."

Owens Corning was found in violation under the catch-all provision.

Lawyers for the company contend in their brief the code is invalid because it invades the Legislature's lawmaking powers and is so vague as to be unconstitutional.

They also argue that the Health Department failed to follow prescribed procedure in enforcing the code. They point out the company has so far spent over $3 million to eliminate phenol and formaldehyde odors from the plant.

However, attorneys for the state reply that the catch-all chapter of the code is essential for prevention of air pollution because it is impossible beforehand to identify and define every type of air pollution.

First Assistant Attorney General Joseph A. Hoffman, who will argue the case for the state, declared in the brief that the Air Pollution Control Act is a valid enactment to promote the public welfare.

He continues:

"It is clear that the law reaches well beyond the traditional standard which prohibited pollutants which were injurious to human or animal health or to property.

"The statute also prescribed any contamination of the air which unreasonably interferes with the comfortable enjoyment of life. It is evident that the Legislature has recognized the critical problem of air pollution in this heavily industrialized state, and has endeavored by this enactment to safeguard not only the health of its citizens but also their right to life in a fresh and clean atmosphere."

The growing public concern about the consequences of pollution is reflected in the action taken in the Congress of the United States and in many state legislative bodies. New regulations, codes, and laws have been adopted that give national and state control agencies more latitude in enforcement and encourage a more vigorous attack on the problem. The Federal Air Quality Act of 1967 (Public Law 90-148), for example, is a blueprint of responsibility and actions to be taken in a systematic effort to deal with pollution on a regional basis. It calls for coordinated action at all levels of government and among all segments of industry.

This Act of 1967 can be used as a model for the control of all forms of pollution. The basic system established by this legislation hinges on the designation of regions where two or more communities—either in the same or different states—share a common pollution problem. Then the key to action is that these communities—working together—are charged with the responsibility of developing and implementing air quality standards for their region. The major features of the Air Quality Act of 1967 are worth noting because the responsibility and steps to be followed are clear and obvious.

• The Department of Health, Education, and Welfare has the responsibility of defining the broad atmospheric areas of the nation and of designating specific air quality control regions.
• The Department is also charged with the responsibility of developing and publishing air pollution criteria indicating the extent to which air pollution is harmful to health and damaging to property. The federal agency must also supply detailed information on the cost and effectiveness of techniques for preventing and controlling air pollution.

• As soon as air quality criteria and data on control technology are made available for a pollutant or class of pollutants, states are required to begin developing air quality standards and plans for implementation of the standards. The state has ninety days to submit a letter indicating that it intends to set standards, 180 days to set the standards, and 180 days to develop plans for implementating them.

• Air quality standards are developed and applied on a regional basis. Wherever an air quality control region includes parts of two or more states, each state is expected to develop standards for its portion of the region.

• If the Secretary of Health, Education, and Welfare finds that the air quality standards and plans for implementation of the standards in an air quality control region are consistent with the provisions of the Air Quality Act, then those standards and plans take effect.

• If a state fails to establish standards or if the Secretary finds that the standards are not consistent with the Act, he can initiate action to insure that appropriate standards are set. States may request a hearing on any standards developed by the Secretary; the hearing board's decision will be binding.

• States are expected to assume the primary responsibility for application of the air quality standards. If a state's efforts prove inadequate, the Secretary is empowered to initiate abatement action.

The most important barrier today that keeps us from cleaning up our environment is an economic one. Effective pollution control simply costs money. Every precaution taken to avoid polluting water is expensive to some water-using industry. And each industry is keenly aware of its competitors at home and abroad. Companies are reluctant to spend large sums of money for equipment from which, in most cases, no competitive advantage is received.

The same economic consideration motivates each community, too. Adequate garbage and sewage disposal costs money. And every homeowner has a natural reluctance about agreeing to raise additional taxes for these services. The money that is

Rural free delivery of mail and a good, blacktop road are signs of progress. But what about the outhouse that stands within fifty feet of that blacktop road? We have our priorities. One of these priorities does not seem to be proper sanitation for all our people.

available from property, income, sales, and other taxes is already divided among so many essential activities, including slum clearance and road building, that there just doesn't seem to be enough to go around.

The problem is to help each citizen and each industrialist recognize the importance of appropriating money for environmental health. We can build more roads only to find that the pollutants from the automobile suffocate us all. We can clear the slums in a ghetto only to find that we have made an environmental slum of the whole world. It is not a matter of priorities in the use of tax money. Nor is it a matter of the profit of an individual industry. It is, in fact, a matter of survival and pride.

A sight we should never see. But we do!

Civic pride and the dislike of ugly and unhealthy surroundings must be the motivations that impel us to raise the taxes necessary at the community level. And an aroused public is the best stimulant to encourage industry to act responsibly and voluntarily to abate their own harmful effluents.

Most environmental problems are the inevitable results of a rapidly expanding population that requires greater industrial and agricultural activity to meet the basic demands for more food, housing, and clothing. The population explosion is real. The world population at the beginning of the 1960s was about three billion. It is growing at the rate of fifty-one million people a year. The population in the year 2000 will more than likely be six billion.

The average rate by which the population is increasing is 1.7 percent per year. Some regions, however, are growing much faster than this. India, for example, jumps at the rate of 2 percent per year. The population of Latin America increases at even a faster rate: 3.5 percent per year, which means that over a twenty-year period covering the 1970s and 1980s, the number of Latin Americans will double.

In 1980, the four nations having the largest populations will be China, India, the Soviet Union, and the United States. China will have a population approaching one billion, India more than 650 million, the Soviet Union a little over 300 million, and the United States will be at about 250 million.

The Soviet Union long ago condemned the need for birth control. It has made the claim that technology can support all the people who are born, and even insists that the increased population of the world will speed economic development. It is true that the world knows how to increase industry and utilize natural resources as demanded. But do we also know how to maintain an environment that will be compatible with this new burden of people?

In the United States the rural population was fifty-four million in 1950, with no change in 1960. Over the next decade, however, the rural population decreased by one million, and stood at fifty-three million in 1970. The projection is that the rural population during the decade of the 1970s will hold at fifty-three million.

But let's take a look at what happened to the urban population in the United States over the same period. There were 97 million people in urban areas in 1950. By 1960, the population of these areas swelled to 125 million. And in 1970, of the 212 million people in this country, some 159 million lived in urban centers. The projection for 1980 is that 197 million people will live in these centers.

At one time the population and the political power in our nation was concentrated in the rural areas. But the picture has changed dramatically. Over the last thirty years, millions of people have been added to our cities. This pressure of concentrating population has had profound effects on our politics and our ability to control environment pollution. Today, we find that population, political power, and pollution too are centered over-whelmingly in the urban areas.

The quality of the urban environment has been deteriorating for years—slowly at first, and now so swiftly that no amount of effort seems to be able to prevent it. Urban renewal programs in our older cities are not making an appreciable difference. Growth and rapid deterioration exist side by side. The spread of super-cities only adds to the problem and makes the renewal effort seem less effective than it really is. Some urban planners visualize the area from Boston to Washington as being well on its way to becoming one of these supercities. Another supercity is taking shape on the West Coast, from San Diego to San Francisco.

The fact before us is that 70 percent of our population is moving into urban areas, which represent only 10 percent of our total land. One of the problems is to learn how to shift population growth away from some areas to others. There are, for example, parts of the country that are not burdened by too many people. These areas can sustain a greater population than they now have or than is projected for them in the immediate future. With a little effort, we can make these locations attractive for people so that we can get a voluntary shift to them. If a shift does not occur, our best efforts at pollution control will be reduced to nothing in the overcrowded areas.

One alternative to urban blight and sprawl is, of course, to start fresh, in a new location. This is the approach being taken in a number of instances. At the beginning of 1970, there were sixty new towns of more than five thousand acres each in various stages of development in the United States. All of these new cities are being planned by private enterprise.

Irvine Ranch in California is one of the largest of the new cities under development. It is in the eighth year of a fifty-year plan to convert eighty-eight thousand acres into a community for five hundred thousand people. It will be a city with eleven self-contained communities.

Columbia, Maryland, is another imaginative plan for the creation of a new city. A key principle that has gone into the planning of Columbia is that industry can be located in the same area where people live without sacrificing open spaces. The projection is that the industry located within the boundaries of the city will provide jobs for as many as three thousand local residents.

There are also a number of experimental plans being funded by federal money. Among these experimenal cities is one that will try many concepts from reusable buildings to underground factories. Horizontal elevators are planned for the transportation of people. These elevators will eliminate air-burning automobiles and buses from the city and thus do away with this source of pollution. Such a city will be somewhat like a space capsule.

A view of Columbia, Maryland.

What will we do with all of our garbage?

Everything—including wastes—will be reconstituted and reusable. The plans call for 250,000 people to live and work on twenty-five hundred acres. If the plan becomes reality it will be a noise-free, pure-air city surrounded by as many as forty thousand acres of insulating open countryside.

Whatever our cities of the future look like, we will need to cope with monumental piles of waste. By the year 2000, we will consume more than thirty-three million tons of canned foods and beverages annually. Our vast container problem will be twice what it is today. We certainly will need to do something to reprocess the containers. Then there will be 475 million tons of paper and 3.2 billion pounds of rigid or molded plastic used in packaging which will need to be reprocessed or disposed

of. The simple fact is that the more people there are, the more
critical our pollution problems are likely to become. The only
possibility we have of coping with our future seems to involve a
complete renovation of our cities and redesigning our industrial
and commercial plants with pollution control in mind.

Rome has had a city water system for the last two thousand
years. But population growth and rapid industrialization in
recent years have taxed the water system to its limit. In the
fall of 1968, one section of Rome was without water for a month.
Naples, Palermo, and other Italian cities were sharing the same
fate as Rome. In fact, more than 41 percent of Italian cities were
without adequate drinking water. This state of affairs has developed because the fairly rich water resources of Italy have
never been fully exploited nor fully protected.

Pollution in all its many forms is a world problem. The pressure
of population growth and industrialization will multiply the
problems in the years ahead. Many of these problems can be
anticipated, and some can be handled by organizations that
cut across national boundaries. One such organization that exists
today is the Pan American Sanitary Bureau. During the last ten
years, it has done a great deal to help Latin American countries
establish adequate water supplies and sewage disposal operations.

The ability of supernational organizations to exist and function
depends on a spirit of cooperation among nations. Unfortunately,
this spirit exists in only a very few cases. One example of
cooperation, however, can be found along the Colorado River,
which runs from the United States into Mexico. U.S. technicians
regularly water down the river to make it less salty as it flows
south of the border. Through the Water Treaty of 1944 between
the United States and Mexico, the United States guarantees that
1.5 million acre-feet of water will flow into Mexico and that the
concentration of salt, including minerals from soil and fertilizers,
will not be excessive. Each year there is a periodic rise in the
salinity of the Colorado water from October through February.
During these months, precipitation is locked in the form of ice
and snow on the mountains. There is less water in the river, and
the salinity rises. Thus, from October to February, there is a
need to add water to the river. Water is pumped from more
than 100 wells to increase the river's flow. The flow of water

increases naturally during the months of April through July, when the snows melt.

A casual glance at the sky of most European cities will tell you that they, too, suffer from air pollution. Some 180,000 tons of pollutants are pumped into Paris skies each year. Nearly three-fourths of the sulphur dioxide poured into the air of Paris comes from heating systems. The central heating systems of the big Paris apartment houses go full blast from October to April. Every section of Paris is occupied by residential apartment houses. There are no districts that empty in the evening after business hours. Parisians live just as thickly around the Paris Stock Exchange and the food market as they do in the night club area. Then, of course, there are the automobiles. The population of cars in Paris is increasing even more rapidly than the human population. And along with the automobiles come carbon monoxide and other pollutants.

London, Rome, Tokyo, and other major cities of the world have pollution problems. No one is safe and no locale is immune. The question is whether we and they will act in time to prevent worldwide tragedy.

Photo Credits

Paul Almazy from World Health Organization, 108. American Cynamid Company from Robertson Studio, 78, 79. Arabian American Oil Company, 74, 155. Max Araujo from Rouse Company, 176. Igor Belyayev from Novosti Press Agency, 66. Bethlehem Steel Corporation, 130, *Call-Cronicle* Newspapers, Allantown, Pennsylvania, 99. Chicago Department of Air Pollution Control, 102. Chicago *Tribune*, 101. ESSA, 7, 18. General Dynamics, 151. General Electric, 93. Goodyear, 122. Humble Oil, 147, 153, 158. National Air Pollution Control Administration, 95. National Medical Audiovisual Center, 81. Celeste Navarra, 22, 22, 26, 29, 33, 55, 56, 61, 63, 88, 104, 104, 111, 116, 121, 126, 132, 132, 137, 137, 139, 139, 141, 144, 149, 159, 160, 161, 172, 173, 177. Skip Nelson from KSTP Films, 14. Nenadovic from UNESCO, 85, 86. Pan American Health Organization, 59. Dominique Roger from UNESCO, 84. Rex Gary Schmidt from United States Department of the Interior, 35. South African Tourist Corporation, 32. United States Department of Agriculture, 38. United States Department of the Interior, 44, 46, 48, 51, 52, 69, 72, 115, 164. The Washington *Post*, 91.

JOHN GABRIEL NAVARRA, the author of *The World You Inherit,* is professor of geo-science and former chairman of the division of science at Jersey City State College. As both a teacher and a writer, Dr. Navarra has an international reputation. He was the teacher of the first televised science course to be offered in the South when he was on the faculty of East Carolina University. He has written a number of trade books for young readers, adult science books, and is the senior author of a complete series of science books, grades kindergarten through nine, that are used by millions of school children throughout the United States. Dr. Navarra traveled extensively to do research on *The World You Inherit.*

INDEX